S0-BRE-383

Fernald Library
Colby-Sawyer College
New London, New Hampshire

Presented By
The Estate of Roger B. Webber

IMAGES OF THE UNIVERSE

IMAGES OF

THE UNIVERSE

LEONARDO DA VINCI: THE ARTIST AS SCIENTIST

by Richard McLanathan

DOUBLEDAY & COMPANY, INC.
GARDEN CITY, NEW YORK

1966

LIBRARY
COLBY-SAWYER COLLEGE
NEW LONDON, N.H. 03257

NC
1055
.L5
M25

11185

Library of Congress Catalog Card Number AC 66–10368
Copyright © 1966 by Richard McLanathan
All Rights Reserved
Printed in the United States of America
First Edition in the United States of America

Endpaper illustrations and jacket detail reproduced by gracious permission of Her Majesty the Queen

97042

IN MEMORY OF ABBOTT PAYSON USHER

CONTENTS

INTRODUCTION BY ABBOTT PAYSON USHER 11

FOREWORD 13

ITALY'S GOLDEN AGE 17

I

Leonardo the Florentine 21

THE YOUNG MAN FROM VINCI 23

AT THE COURT OF LUDOVICO THE MOOR 37

THE UNSETTLED YEARS 51

II

"I Wish to Work Miracles" 69

"THE AIR IS FILLED WITH COUNTLESS IMAGES" 71

"THE VITAL HUMOR OF THIS ARID EARTH" 87

"MANY MOST POWERFUL MACHINES OF WAR" 103

"THE GREAT BIRD WILL TAKE ITS FLIGHT" 135

"THE PARADISE OF MATHEMATICAL SCIENCES" 145

III

"Man Is the Image of the World" 167

IMPORANT DATES IN LEONARDO'S LIFE AND TIMES 183

A SHORT LIST OF BOOKS 187

INDEX 189

LIST OF ILLUSTRATIONS

Twenty-seven Cats and a Dragon, c. 1507–8. Royal Library, Windsor 22
A Dog and Two Cats. British Museum, London 24
An Ox and an Ass, c. 1480. Royal Library, Windsor 26
Hanging Body of Bernardo di Bandino Baroncelli, 1478. Musée Bonnat, Bayonne 27
The Valley of the Arno, 1473. Uffizi, Florence 31
Study of a Woman's Hands, c. 1478–80. Royal Library, Windsor 32
Profile of a Warrior, c. 1475. British Museum, London 33
The Head of the Virgin, c. 1480. Louvre, Paris 34
Angel's Head, c. 1480. Royal Library, Turin 35
Study for the Sforza Monument, 1488. Royal Library, Windsor 36
Sketch for *The Last Supper,* c. 1495. Royal Library, Windsor 39
Design for a Stable, c. 1488–89. Institut de France, Paris 40
Study for an Ideal City, c. 1488–89. Institut de France, Paris 40
Studies for *The Virgin and Holy Children,* 1482–83. The Metropolitan Museum, New York 42
Studies of Flowers, c. 1483. Academy, Venice 43
Studies of Horses for the Sforza Monument, c. 1488. Royal Library, Windsor 44
Designs for a Domed Church, 1488–89. Institut de France, Paris 45
A Study from Nature for the Sforza Monument, 1490. Royal Library, Windsor 46
Study for St. James the Greater in *The Last Supper,* 1495–96. Royal Library, Windsor 47
Study for *The Last Supper,* 1495–97. Academy, Venice 48
Neptune in his Chariot, 1504. Royal Library, Windsor 52
Fighting Horsemen, 1503–4. Academy, Venice 54
Dragons. Royal Library, Windsor 56
A Dog. Royal Library, Windsor 58
Portrait Sketch of Cesare Borgia from Three Sides, 1502. Royal Library, Turin 60
Spray of a Plant, c. 1505–8. Royal Library, Windsor 61
Studies for *St. George and the Dragon,* 1507–8. Royal Library, Windsor 63
Study of Drapery for *The Madonna and Child with St. Anne,* c. 1501. Louvre, Paris. 64
Studies for the Equestrian Monument of Gian Giacomo Trivulzio, 1511–12. Royal Library, Windsor 65
Masquerader in Costume, c. 1513. Royal Library, Windsor 66
A Sketch of Amboise, c. 1516. Royal Library, Windsor 67
Illustration by Leonardo for *The Divine Proportion,* Venice, 1509 70
Detail of Leonardo's Projector. Ambrosiana, Milan 71
Landscape with a River and a Canal, c. 1503. Royal Library, Windsor 72
Bird's-eye View of a Castle from a Map of the Arezzo Area. Ambrosiana, Milan 73
Anatomy of a Leg in Exploded Sections. Royal Library, Windsor 73
Study for *The Adoration of the Magi,* 1481. Louvre, Paris 77
A Square Church with Dome and Minarets, c. 1488–89. Bibliothèque Nationale, Paris 78
Studies of Mountain Ranges, c. 1511. Royal Library, Windsor 79

Study of a Tree, c. 1498. Royal Library, Windsor 80
Anatomical Drawing of a Skull, 1489. Royal Library, Windsor 81
Anatomical Study of a Man's Leg and a Dog's, c. 1504. Royal Library, Windsor 82
Anatomical Study of a Man's Shoulder, 1510. Royal Library, Windsor 83
Dissection of the Principal Organs of a Woman, c. 1510. Royal Library, Windsor 85
Storm Breaking over an Alpine Valley, c. 1499. Royal Library, Windsor 86
Old Man Meditating, and Studies of Swirling Water, c. 1510. Royal Library, Windsor 88
Dredge, c. 1475–80. Ambrosiana, Milan 89
Studies of Diving Equipment and a Device for Underwater Attack on Ships, c. 1500. Ambrosiana, Milan 91
Detail of Man in a Life Preserver. Ambrosiana, Milan 91
Detail of Man Walking on Water, Ambrosiana, Milan 91
Detail of Diver's Breathing Tube. Ambrosiana, Milan 91
Outcrop of Stratified Rock, c. 1510–13. Royal Library, Windsor 93
Various Devices for Raising Water, c. 1475–80. Ambrosiana, Milan 94
Canal with Two Locks, c. 1475–80. Ambrosiana, Milan 97
A Lock Gate for a Canal, c. 1475–80. Ambrosiana, Milan 99
Double Crane, c. 1475–80. Ambrosiana, Milan 101
Courtyard of a Foundry, c. 1487. Royal Library, Windsor 102
Detail of a Coil-Spring Arrow Shooter. Ambrosiana, Milan 105
Detail of a Wheel of Cannon. Ambrosiana, Milan 106
Cannon Construction, c. 1485–88. Ambrosiana, Milan 106
Detail of a Bomb about to Explode. Ambrosiana, Milan 107
Detail of Circular Fortress with Concentric Encientes. Ambrosiana, Milan 107
A Chariot Armed with Scythes, and a Tank, c. 1485–88. British Museum, London 109
Two Chariots Armed with Scythes, c. 1485–88. Royal Library, Turin 110
Chariots Armed with Flails and War Clubs, a Bowman with a Shield, and a Horseman with Three Lances, c. 1485–88. Royal Library, Windsor 111
Giant Crossbow on Wheels, c. 1485–88. Ambrosiana, Milan 113
Bombards Firing Shells and Caltrops, c. 1485–88. Ambrosiana, Milan 114
Studies of Shields for Foot Soldiers and of a Bomb, c. 1485–88. École des Beaux-Arts, Paris 115
Crossbows Mounted in a Wheel, c. 1485–88. Ambrosiana, Milan 116
Two Types of Catapult and a Ballista, c. 1485–88. Ambrosiana, Milan 117
A Centrifugal Mangonel with Eight Arms, c. 1485–88. Ambrosiana, Milan 118
A Spring Catapult, c. 1485–88. Ambrosiana, Milan 119
Study Showing the Stages in the Construction of a Cannon, c. 1485–88. Ambrosiana, Milan 120
Studies of Mortars and Cannon, c. 1485–88. Royal Library, Windsor 121
Three Types of Multibarreled Cannon, c. 1485–88. Ambrosiana, Milan 123
The *Architronito* or Steam Cannon, c. 1485–88. Institut de France, Paris 124
Foot Soldiers with Shielded Lances Attacking Horsemen, and Various Weapons, c. 1485–88. Academy, Venice 125
Assault Ladders, c. 1485–88. Ambrosiana, Milan 127
A Device for Repelling Scaling Ladders, c. 1475–80. Ambrosiana, Milan 128
Three Types of Swinging Bridge, c. 1485–88. Ambrosiana, Milan 129
A Siege Tower, c. 1485–88. Ambrosiana, Milan 131
Drawings of Fortifications, c. 1485–88. Ambrosiana, Milan 132
Drawing of a Flying Machine with Operator, c. 1500. Institut de France, Paris 134
Detail of Parachute. Royal Library, Turin 135

Detail of Helicopter. Royal Library, Turin 135
A Wing on a Test Block, c. 1490. Institut de France, Paris 136
A Flying Machine, c. 1490. Institut de France, Paris 136
Drawing of a Flying Machine, c. 1490. Ambrosiana, Milan 139
Study of the Structure of a Wing, c. 1490. Ambrosiana, Milan 140
Study of the Construction of a Flexible Wing, c. 1495. Ambrosiana, Milan 141
Study of the Construction and Control of a Wing, c. 1490. Ambrosiana, Milan 143
File-making Machine, c. 1490. Ambrosiana, Milan 144
Detail of a Pulley. Ambrosiana, Milan 146
Detail of a Threading Tool. Ambrosiana, Milan 147
Screw-cutting Machine. Institut de France, Paris 147
Detail of an Earth Borer. Ambrosiana, Milan 148
Detail of a Friction Transmission. Ambrosiana, Milan 148
Detail of Gears. Ambrosiana, Milan 148
Detail of a Pendulum. Ambrosiana, Milan 150
Detail of an Hodometer. Ambrosiana, Milan 150
Two Lifting Devices. Ambrosiana, Milan 152
Studies of Gear Systems and Transmission Devices. Ambrosiana, Milan 153
Sketch of a Printing Press, c. 1485–90. Ambrosiana, Milan 154
Two Types of Turnspit. Ambrosiana, Milan 155
Machine for Drawing Thin Strips of Metal, c. 1485–90. Institut de France, Paris 156
Machine for Drawing Iron Bars, c. 1485–95. Ambrosiana, Milan 157
Spinning Machine with Flyer, c. 1485. Ambrosiana, Milan 158
Nap-raising Machine, c. 1485. Ambrosiana, Milan 159
Studies of a Lathe, Olive-oil Press, and Worm Gearing, c. 1485–95. Ambrosiana, Milan. 161
An Earth-moving Machine, c. 1485. Ambrosiana, Milan 163
Automatic Hammer, 1515–16. Ambrosiana, Milan. 165
Proportions of the Human Figure after Vitruvius, c. 1492. Academy, Venice 168
Study for *Leda and the Swan,* c. 1506. Royal Library, Windsor 170
Oak Leaves with Acorns and Dyer's Greenweed. Royal Library, Windsor 171
Study for *The Battle of Anghiari,* 1503–4. Academy, Venice 172
Cloudburst, after 1514. Royal Library, Windsor 173
An Embryo in the Uterus, c. 1512. Royal Library, Windsor 175
A Star of Bethlehem and Other Plants, c. 1505–8. Royal Library, Windsor 176
Studies of Water, c. 1510. Royal Library, Windsor 177
Studies in Expression: Horses, a Lion, a Man, c. 1503–4. Royal Library, Windsor 178
Leonardo's Self-portrait, c. 1512. Royal Library, Turin 180
Deluge, c. 1517. Royal Library, Windsor 181

INTRODUCTION

Although there has been a steady growth in the literature on Leonardo da Vinci, this new study gives a more vivid insight into the character of Leonardo and his methods of work than most of the biographies and critical essays. Mr. McLanathan has made a judicious selection of drawings from the notebooks and elsewhere, confining the text to a biographical sketch and a short description of the major classes of work in science, technology, and engineering.

The drawings from the notebooks are reproduced without reduction and as nearly as possible in the color of the original manuscripts, and the captions combine translations from Leonardo's own notes and the author's supplementary descriptions. All the notebooks have, of course, been reproduced and the text has been transcribed and translated, but the amount of this material is so great that it is obtainable only in the largest libraries. This volume, however, gives a reader an opportunity to study at leisure a representative selection from a great mass of material spread among many collections, and without the necessity of constantly turning to the translations of Richter and MacCurdy.

The notebooks were intended to serve as a basis for systematic treatises on painting, the problems of hydraulics, and the flight of birds, and the general principles of mechanics, both static and dynamic. The manuscript on the flight of birds is the only "treatise" put together by Leonardo himself. That on painting is a compilation, sometimes attributed to his pupil Orazio Melzi from material in the notebooks. Studies of hydraulics and mechanics were utilized by Girolamo Cardano and others without acknowledgment of their indebtedness.

Leonardo began many things, but left an extraordinary amount of unfinished work. It is for this reason that it is so important to appreciate the intensity of his desire to make fresh observations of the world about him; to free himself from the domination of books; and to obtain immediate knowledge of human nature and the external world. He was always anxious to establish general principles, but he was not satisfied that his observations were complete, and systematic composition was ever being postponed to secure more material. Had his interests been narrower, he might well have concentrated on a particular problem or problems and made more of a synthesis in a limited field. But his insatiable curiosity always led him on.

Without his talent for drawing he would have had to take refuge in words, and the limitation of such a vehicle of expression would probably have forced him to concentrate on a limited field. His skill as a draughtsman made it possible for him to express every observation in visual images. In his studies of anatomy he placed great emphasis on the superiority of drawings made from several points of view over any possible text description. Any mechanism he conceived could be accurately and completely represented in one or more drawings. The drawings of mechanisms are essentially analytical;

only the primary features are shown, without supporting frames and settings. The drawings are, therefore, a characteristic feature of the notebooks, and it is necessary to maintain an exact balance between the drawings and the text. Mr. McLanathan has been extraordinarily successful in keeping this balance.

The biographical sketch emphasizes the contrast between Florence under the Medici and Milan under the Sforza. It is tempting to think of Florence as Leonardo's home, and some feel that Leonardo can best be characterized as the Florentine. But we must recognize that the seventeen years spent in Florence were followed by an equal span of years spent in Milan. The ostentation of life at court there was supplemented by the contacts afforded by the University at Pavia and by the important group of scholars at the court itself. It is wise, therefore, not to presume that the acceptance of service with Sforza led to a major change in the distribution of Leonardo's activities among his varied interests. The range of his work was fully established before he left Florence, and there were notable achievements in every phase of his work in the years spent at Milan.

In all probability, Leonardo gave more time to civil and military engineering at Milan than would have been the case had he remained in Florence. The old canals of Lombardy invited further development, and the political unrest made military expenditure necessary on both offensive weapons and defensive equipment. Without this experience in Milan under Sforza, Leonardo might have had little interest in the problems of Venice with the Turks or in the invitation to take charge of the military enterprises of Cesare Borgia. The ten years in French service at Milan and Amboise also involved engineering work, both civil and military, anatomical research, and projects in painting, sculpture, and architecture.

The fertility of his imagination made Leonardo highly suggestible to all the requirements of his duties, but new tasks did not distract him from the broad objectives formulated early in his life. Throughout his life his mind was constantly turning from one problem to another. Single sheets in the notebooks often have several totally different items tucked away wherever there is any unused space. So it is important to emphasize the continuing diversity of Leonardo's interests rather than to impose on all this material our present judgments of the relative value and significance of the different categories of his work.

ABBOTT PAYSON USHER

Sea Turn, Castine, Maine

Professor Abbott Payson Usher was the author of a number of major works on economic history, including the definitive *History of Mechanical Inventions,* first published in 1920 and again in a revised edition in 1954. A graduate of Harvard, where he received his A.M. and Ph.D., he also studied at the University of Paris, and was Professor of Economics at Cornell, the University of Wisconsin, and Boston University before joining the Harvard faculty in 1922. He was also Visiting Professor of Economic History at Wisconsin, Yale, and elsewhere. He contributed numerous articles to various publications in the field, and in 1963 was awarded the Leonardo da Vinci Medal by the Society for the History of Technology.

FOREWORD

There is considerable variation in the size of Leonardo's notebooks, but the greater number of them, especially those dealing with scientific and engineering subjects, come close to averaging the size chosen for the pages of this book so that all the notebook pages and details from them can be reproduced at the actual scale of the originals. Many individual drawings are on sheets of different sizes, and when possible they, too, have been reproduced at true scale. Thus all but a handful of the illustrations are the same size as Leonardo's original works, and therefore dimensions are given only for those few that have had to be reduced to fit the page.

Most of his notes and sketches were made in pen and ink, but other mediums appear, especially among the drawings, where he often used black chalk, red chalk, ink wash, and silverpoint or metalpoint, similar to a modern hard pencil but capable of a finer line, and various combinations of them. The paper he generally preferred was a fine-textured white paper—necessary because of the small scale of most of his sketches. But colored papers also occur, though for a colored background he usually used paper prepared according to a standard practice of the period, with a colored ground laid on the surface. This has been noted in the captions.

After undergoing a most varied history, Leonardo's notebooks, separated and recombined until the order of many of the pages is completely confused, now are gathered in a few collections. The *Codex Atlanticus,* so called from its vast size and scope, is in the Ambrosian Library in Milan; other sections are in the Library of the Institut de France and the Bibliothèque Nationale in Paris, the Royal Library in Turin, the British Museum, the Vatican Library in Rome, the Pierpont Morgan Library in New York, and elsewhere. Many of the individual drawings are scattered among European museums and collections, including the Louvre in Paris, the Academy in Venice, and the Uffizi in Florence, with the finest concentration of them in the Royal Library at Windsor Castle.

A tremendous amount has been written about Leonardo, a small selection of which is listed in the rear of this book. But everyone who wishes to approach any aspect of his diverse career must turn to the translations of his writings by Jean Paul and Irma A. Richter, and by Edward MacCurdy. This book, like every other recent study of him, has depended on the work of these scholars, and the many quotations that appear in the captions and the text are based upon it, with only an occasional change where it seemed necessary for clarity in contemporary terms. Information on the drawings has been derived from A. E. Popham's general catalogue and Sir Kenneth Clark's catalogue of those at Windsor, while the chronology and interpretation of the record of his life follow the latter author's *Leonardo da Vinci, an Account of His Development as an Artist,* which is a model of its kind.

There are three major collections of study material pertaining to Leonardo in the United States: the Elmer Belt Library at the University of California in Los Angeles, the John W. Lieb Memorial Collection at Stevens Institute of Technology in Hoboken, New Jersey, and the Burndy Library in Norwalk, Connecticut.

Through its Division of Arts and Sciences, the International Business Machines Corporation circulates exhibitions of models of various machines and devices from Leonardo's notebooks and has published a related brochure.

The Leonardo da Vinci National Museum of Science and Technology in Milan has displays illustrating his technical and scientific achievements, and the Château of Clos-Lucé, formerly the Manor of Cloux, at Amboise, France, has been restored by its owner to the condition that it was in when Leonardo spent the last years of his life there and is now open to the public.

Many persons gave valuable advice and assistance during the preparation of this book. First among those who deserve particular acknowledgment is the late Abbott Payson Usher, whose encouragement and interest, critical and kindly scrutiny of the manuscript, and substantial contribution of the Introduction suggest something of both the scholarship and the generosity of spirit that won him universal respect. Professor Irwin Panofsky of the Institute for Advanced Studies, Princeton, was most helpful, as were Miss Aidua H. Scott-Elliot, Keeper of Prints and Drawings in the Royal Library at Windsor Castle; A. Hyatt Mayor, Curator of Prints, Jacob Bean, Curator of Drawings, John Goldsmith Phillips, Curator of Western European Art, and Emanuel Winternitz, Curator of Musical Instruments, all of the Metropolitan Museum of Art in New York; Richard Collins, Manager of the Division of Arts and Sciences, International Business Machines Corporation; Mme. Sylvie Beguin of the Department of Paintings of the Louvre; Jean Adhémar, Director of the Bibliothèque Nationale, Paris; Dr. Francesco Valcanover, Director of the Galleries of the Academy, Venice; and J. C. Lemoine, Curator of the Musée Bonnat, Bayonne.

Special thanks are due to Her Majesty the Queen for gracious permission to reproduce drawings from the Royal Library at Windsor, to the officers of the various institutions who have granted the reproduction of works in their collections as illustrations, and to their photographic departments for their promptness and cooperation. I am grateful to Irwin Panofsky for permission to quote from his essay "Artist, Scientist, Genius," and to Dudley T. Easby, Jr., for permission to quote from George Sarton's "The Quest for Truth," which appeared in the Metropolitan Museum's *The Renaissance: A Symposium* in 1953.

Aid and information were generously given by many, among them Signora Alberta Fabris of the Italian Cultural Institute in New York; Signora Manoleta T. Doelger and Signor Gianmaria Carretti of the Italian State Tourist Office, New York; D. H. Couvée, Keeper of the Department of National History, Rijksmuseum, Amsterdam; Miss Dorothy Bishop, Miss Lee Plotzman, and Mrs. Suzanne Crowley, all of the Department of Arts and Sciences of the International Business Machines Corporation; Professor Merton C. Flemmings of the Metallurgy Department of the Massachusetts Institute of Technology; Count Hubert Saint-Bris of Clos-Lucé, Amboise; F. Gordon Morrill of Florence; Mr. and Mrs. Lee Boltin; Leo Mattersdorf; Lino Lepinsky de Orlov; Mrs. Kathryn Canaday; and W. Wallace Benjamin. To all who have contributed to the many aspects of the project go the author's most appreciative thanks. But, finally, for unfailing interest and encouragement, constructive criticism, and devoted practical assistance, my deepest and continuing debt of gratitude is to my wife.

RICHARD McLANATHAN

New York
September 1965

IMAGES OF THE UNIVERSE

ITALY'S GOLDEN AGE

Leonardo da Vinci became a legend during his lifetime. Though few of his pictures are left, he has always been considered among the world's greatest painters. Though no remaining sculpture can with the least certainty be attributed to him, he has always ranked among the leaders in this field. And though his writings were never organized beyond fragmentary notebook jottings and remained unpublished until long after his time, he has always been admired as among the small group of the world's most daring pioneers of thought.

He was courted by the greatest princes, and served for a brief time one of the most murderous despots in history. But he himself considered war the work of madmen and was so kindhearted that he bought cages of wild songbirds in the market place so that he could set them free, and ate no meat because he did not believe in taking life. He was so strong that he could twist a horseshoe as easily as if it were made of lead, was an expert swordsman who never drew a weapon in anger, was a famous musician, and could accomplish feats of physical skill with an ease and grace most could not match after long practice.

In the midst of the violence and ferment of one of the most exciting periods in history, he remained aloof. He confided only to his numerous notebooks—later to be sought after, stolen, purchased, and treasured as if they were so many holy relics—theories, drawings, diagrams, fragmentary ideas, and extraordinary insights. These were the products of a mind more curious and far-ranging than any other we know, and an imagination that soared with birds in flight and into space among the stars, that sought the secrets of earth and sea and those hidden deep within the human body. His energy and his amazing talents were dedicated to a lifetime's search for truth, the truth of nature, of man, of matter, of the forces of life itself.

Though Leonardo da Vinci was a solitary person, he was, as we all are, a product of his times, even though the times can never account for the appearance of genius. So first let us look at the world of brilliance and violence in which he lived, a world that recognized his genius but could never really understand the man, even though it provided opportunities for the development of his talents at the same time that it denied the realization of his greatest hopes. That realization was to be deferred in part to our own times, and in still greater part to a yet more distant future.

The fifteenth century saw the final collapse of the medieval world with its principles of chivalry, so seldom lived up to; of law, so often disregarded; of social order, so neat in theory but so disrupted in fact; and of faith, so elevated and otherworldly in its ideals. A reaction was inevitable. This reaction has been called the Renaissance, or rebirth, because it looked to historians of the day as if men were awakening after a long sleep to the beauties and wonders of this world instead of regarding it as merely a dreary preparation for the next. Actually, it had been emerging gradually for more than a hundred years, but by the fifteenth century the Renaissance was in full flood. It started in Italy and spread northward throughout Europe, bringing profound changes wherever it went, and producing a different world, from which emerged a sense of the worth and dignity of man in which Leonardo so believed. It rediscovered man as an individual, full of extraordinary capacities for good or for ill, but free to follow his own star.

Except for the important developments in the twelfth and thirteenth centuries in clocks and related mechanisms, in a way that was to have profound consequences in the Renaissance and later, there had been little constructive change in science and technology for more than a thousand years. Then, starting with Leonardo's period, came a flashfire of progress that included Galileo's achievements in astronomy in the sixteenth century and Newton's mathematical demonstration of an ordered universe in the seventeenth, to transform the world into what we recognize today. Leonardo stands at the beginning of this transitional period and spans the medieval and the modern eras. Because the main task of science at that time was to regain what had been lost, the Renaissance was a period of synthesis—of putting things together and relating them—not a time of specialization like our own. Then it was possible to aspire to the command of the whole range of human knowledge. More perhaps than anyone in history since the Greeks, Leonardo came closest to achieving that proud ambition. Yet both his extremely acute observations and his instincts told him that there was virtually no end to the ramifications of science; at the same time they suggested to him the idea that there was a basic and central principle or series of principles that held the key to the whole. Ever since his time specialization has increased as knowledge has grown more complex. The various fields of science have multiplied and become fragmented until the vocabularies used to describe them are often virtually unintelligible to laymen—and are mutually exclusive as well. Leonardo lived at a wonderful moment in history when man could try anything and hope for everything, when the world and the universe lay before him for his conjecture and exploration.

There were certain accepted bounds to that world, however. The universe, according to the Greek philosopher Aristotle, was made up of the four elements: earth, air, fire, and water. These were associated with four qualities: dryness, wetness, heat, and cold. All were brought into various combinations by the basic forces of attraction and repulsion, thus producing what we see around us. The Church accepted the Aristotelian theory that the earth is the center, forever fixed and immovable, around which revolve nine concentric, transparent spheres. These are the spheres of the moon, closest to the earth, then of Mercury, Venus, the sun, Mars, Jupiter, and Saturn, then the sphere of the fixed stars, and finally that of the *primum mobile,* the force that turns the spheres from east to west, each revolution taking twenty-four hours.

When one considers the difficulty in our own generation in grasping and understanding the concepts of endless space and astronomic time, we can perhaps understand the shocking philosophical jolt for thoughtful men of the sixteenth century in having this tidy earth-centered system shattered.

During Leonardo's lifetime the Polish astronomer Nicolaus Kopernik, who had studied at the University of Padua, did the greater part of the work which led to his statement of the Copernican system, a revival, after nearly two thousand years, of the theory of Aristarchus of Samos, which placed the sun at the center of the universe, with the planets, including the earth, revolving around it. Kopernik's theory could not have been known to Leonardo, since the Polish scientist's great work was not completed until after Leonardo's death. Yet we find in the notebooks the significant statement, "The sun does not move"; and another note that "the earth is not the center of the circuit of the sun, nor in the center of the universe . . ." so Leonardo, too, was clearly groping toward a similar concept.

Thus the world in which Leonardo lived was a dynamically enlarging one. Ideas of the universe were expanding. Men's notions of the earth were changing. Having revived the Greek concept of it as a globe, they proceeded to prove it by sailing around it. Columbus reached the islands off the coast of America in 1492, the year in which Lorenzo the Magnificent died. Vespucci reached the American mainland in 1497, the same year in which Vasco da Gama sailed around the Cape of Good Hope to India. Cabot reached Newfoundland shortly after, and in 1513, Balboa, having hacked his way through the jungles of the Isthmus, stood, "silent upon a peak in Darien," and looked out in wonder on the limitless expanse of the Pacific. All this happened during Leonardo's lifetime, and by 1600 the surface of the earth known to man was doubled.

It was a time so vibrant with change, so stimulating to those of free mind and spirit, that never since the Great Period of the Greece of Pericles had there been such a flowering of art and literature. Old patterns were shattered, and determined and gifted men found scope for their ambitions, whether to rule a state, write an epic, or paint a fresco. It was as if everyone were living twice as fast and twice as vividly as ever before, determined to cram as much of the richness of life as possible into a short span of years. Art was everywhere and everything was art: dressing was an art, as was war, lovemaking, diplomacy, letter writing, or governing. The air was filled with the music of lutes and trumpets, the streets with the constant pageant of activities of a life more varied and lively than any the world had yet seen. This was the age into which Leonardo was born and in which he lived. Even in his own time he was recognized as a supreme embodiment of its ideals.

It was an age that owed much to the Greeks, and Leonardo shared their indefatigable curiosity and deep respect for nature in all its manifestations. Yet he was a man of a different time and brought to his studies of man and nature a sense of Gothic mystery in his feeling for the independent and inexpressible vastness of existence and of time. Like other men of the Renaissance he, too, was an explorer, but he alone brought an artist's discipline, experience, and perception to an exploration of science, and thus was unique in history.

In the course of this search, Leonardo made observations of the sun and moon, the action of water, of vision, light, and sound; of the structure of rocks and the anatomy of men and animals; of the growth of plants, the force of gravity, the art of war, and the craft of the architect, the sculptor, and the painter. In almost every area of thought he made an original contribution, but perhaps nowhere as much as in science and engineering. He was constantly thinking up devices to test theories or to solve mechanical problems, from lens grinders to machine guns, from a variable-speed drive to an air-conditioning unit, and from a self-propelled vehicle to a flying machine, from measuring the heights of mountains to building an unsinkable ship. He kept a record of everything, in drawings and notes in his distinctive mirror writing, on the countless pages of his notebooks, most of which, fortunately, have been preserved. Despite the incredible variety, each such idea, whether expressed as a principle or as a mechanical device, bears the stamp of his penetrating and original mind, and is a part of his grand-scheme of exploration.

In looking at the record of inexhaustible inventiveness revealed by his drawings, we can share the excitement of that search to which he devoted his life. We can recapture something of the spirit of a man whose hunches have so often turned out to be truer than many of the reasoned theories of others, whose artistic achievement has long been honored, but whose scientific achievement can perhaps begin to be fully appreciated only in our own time. For ours, too, is a period of exploration which is making the first tentative moves out into space, beginning to penetrate the inner workings of the mind of man, and grope toward an understanding of the basic structure of things and the forces that shape and govern them.

I

Leonardo the Florentine

The Young Man from Vinci

On a day in April 1452 Leonardo was born in Anchiano, a tiny village near the hill town of Vinci, just west of Florence. His father was a young notary, or lawyer, of the town, and his mother was a village girl named Caterina. The boy was illegitimate, but that was no cause for shame in those days, and the baby's grandfather recorded that he was christened by the priest of the town in the presence of the family and a number of friends. As a little boy he seems to have stayed with his mother before being taken into his father's house, where he was raised by his father's young wife with a generous kindness that was not rare in those more tolerant times.

His boyhood was spent in Vinci, which remains today much as it was when Leonardo knew it, protected by its battlemented walls, within which are crowded the houses, facing on narrow winding streets. There is a main square with the castle of the Lord of Anchiano and the town church, whose bells still call the people to service, as in Leonardo's day. Outside the fortified gate lies the Tuscan countryside, the slopes of the hills covered as far as one can see with vineyards and groves of olive trees, their leaves silvery in the sunlight. A road winds down the valley toward the Arno River and the highway, important then as now, which connects Florence with Pisa, to the eastward near the sea.

As a boy Leonardo seems to have been left free to roam the country, and it was surely then that his lifelong fascination with the natural world was born, his interest in the flight of birds, the patterns of growth of plants and trees, the habits of animals, both domestic and wild, his love of dogs and cats—and also of horses, for he could ride steeds that no one else could approach. His stepmother was childless, and from the few hints of his early years found in his notebooks, he was a lonely boy who grew up to be a lonely man, set apart from others not only by his genius, for genius is always solitary, but also by the life of exploration and search which he determined to follow.

When Leonardo was about thirteen his father moved to Florence. It must have been a profound change from the little town of Vinci with its few dozen houses, because of all the cities of the Renaissance, it was the most brilliant. It was a city in a ferment of activity, its streets full of people, its shops and markets crowded, and its feast days brilliant with processions. The capital of the ancient region of Tuscany, Florence had long been the intellectual capital of Italy as well. It was the home of her greatest poet, Dante, author of *The Divine Comedy,* and of her greatest artists from Giotto, who was Dante's medieval contemporary to Michelangelo, who was to be born a quarter of a century after Leonardo. The city had flourished for years under the wise and discreet government

Twenty-seven Cats and a Dragon, c. 1507–8. Silverpoint and pen. Windsor; reproduced by gracious permission of Her Majesty the Queen

of the merchant-banker Cosimo de' Medici, a lover and patron of the arts, who numbered among his closest friends Donatello, the greatest sculptor of the period, and Brunelleschi, the greatest architect. When Leonardo moved to Florence, Cosimo had just recently died, but had left a son and two grandsons to carry on his tradition.

Though the city was a thriving center of trade, it lay far from the sea in the valley of the Arno. As when Leonardo first saw it, Giotto's bell tower still rises against the sky close to the cathedral whose vast dome dominates the whole city. Clustered around it are the golden palaces, churches, houses, and other buildings, their roofs mellow with tiles of soft red and dull orange, all set in a countryside extending from the heights of Fiesole, once an ancient Etruscan stronghold, to the hills to the south, with orchards and farmland between slopes covered with vineyards, above which are fortified villas and watchtowers. The city has none of the oriental opulence of Venice nor the magnificence of Rome, but its beautifully proportioned architecture, whether of house or palace, church or guildhall, expresses the clarity of mind and the practicality and distinction of the Florentine character. The Arno flows through the city, its waters a swirling flood swollen with the melting snows of the Apennines in the spring, and diminishing to a trickle in late summer. It was spanned by several bridges, one of which, the famous Ponte Vecchio, or "old bridge," its narrow road lined with houses and shops, was ancient in Leonardo's day, and still links the opposite shores.

A year or so after his family had settled in Florence, a great change took place in Leonardo's life. He had early shown an unusual ability to draw and to model, and seemed more interested in such things than most boys of his age. So his father apprenticed him to one of the most distinguished artists of the time who was called Verrocchio, which means "true eye," by his friends, and has been so known ever since. Like almost all the Florentine artists of his generation, Verrocchio's first training had been as a goldsmith, one of the reasons for the extraordinarily high standard of craftsmanship typical of the art of Florence of the period, but he had gone on to become a painter and an architect and was the city's leading sculptor.

"All our knowledge," Leonardo later wrote, "has its origin in our perceptions," and from his boyhood in Vinci he seems to have been a naturally acute observer who was constantly sharpening his perceptions through an intense and all-embracing curiosity. When he entered Verrocchio's shop a whole new area of experience was opened to him. There he saw men who were masters of the techniques of woodcarving. He saw how they selected a piece of

A Dog and Two Cats. Silverpoint on buff prepared paper. British Museum, London

stock for a given job, judged it for grain and dryness, chose their tools, sharpened them, and then proceeded to cut away the wood to reveal the three-dimensional form of a Madonna or a saint, a garland of fruit and flowers, a wreath of foliage for a frame, or an architectural setting for an altarpiece. He saw how the wood, whether carved or a panel for a painting, was coated with gesso, a fine white plaster. He learned how the gilder worked, running his brush through his hair to give it just enough static electricity to pick up one of the sheets of pure gold, beaten by hand to an unbelievable thinness, and then lay it in place, later to be burnished to a shining brilliance with a piece of polished hematite or agate.

He learned how colors were made, the pigments ground in mortars, and then applied with the yolk of an egg to the specially prepared panel to form the firmest and most permanent kind of painting man has yet devised. He saw the preparation of oil of walnuts, or of flax or hemp seeds, for the transparent glazes of color which added richness and subtlety to the painting of the Renaissance under the influence of a technique, then newly introduced into Italy, which had been developed by artists of the Netherlands. He learned how papers were tinted for drawings to be made with a silverpoint, how charcoal was prepared from sprigs of grapevine for laying in a design on the pure white of a gessoed panel, and how to erase it with a chicken feather for corrections. He saw how ink was made of lampblack or the galls of oak trees, and how to make brushes from the tails of minivers and pens from goose quills.

He saw all the craft of the goldsmith: the preparation of the metal, the raising of the form through hammering with the constant annealing in flame to prevent brittleness, the engraving of the surface, and the casting and joining of parts. He learned how to sculpture in terra cotta and to prepare the wax for making the small models for larger sculptures; how to construct armatures, the skeletons for the plaster or clay figures to be cast in bronze; and all the inherited techniques of metallurgy, with its mysteries of moldmaking and alloys; of smithery, with welding, chasing, and embossing; of illumination of parchment or vellum, the selecting, cutting, and shaping of stone from large sculptures in marble to tiny gems; how to draw for embroiderers; paint and gild on glass; make a life mask; prepare a wall and paint a fresco; and how to make surgical instruments and design special tools to perform all sorts of delicate tasks.

As in a Florentine shop today, the youngest apprentice started with the most simple and menial tasks—running errands, sweeping up, making himself generally useful—and then was gradually entrusted with greater responsibilities until he was allowed to undertake some sort of work on his own under the watchful eye of one of the journeymen or the master himself. Thus artists learned by seeing and by doing; they learned both practice and theory at the same time, and could go at whatever pace and as far as their abilities and ambitions would allow.

During Leonardo's years of apprenticeship, Verrocchio made and gilded a great copper ball, which was hoisted into place to the chanting of the Te Deum on May 27, 1471, and still surmounts the cupola of the cathedral. He produced large-scale sculptures in bronze for the Guild of the Wool Merchants, a sarcophagus of marble, porphyry, and bronze for Piero and Giovanni de' Medici, a number of paintings, and innumerable other miscellaneous commissions, probably including some in architecture. And he was in the midst of making the bronze equestrian statue of Colleoni for the city of Venice when Leonardo left for Milan. Since Florence was still a small enough town so that artists and craftsmen all knew one another, Leonardo undoubtedly saw much of what was going on in other shops. With this kind of training, probably unattainable at that time anywhere except in Florence, and rare enough there because few took on such a variety of tasks as Verrocchio, Leonardo had a unique background for his scientific and mechanical studies.

All his life he regretted the lack of education in Latin and Greek, which he felt excluded him from the brilliant circle of scholars and poets who were Lorenzo's favorite companions. But it was in Verrocchio's shop, rather than at the meetings of the Platonic Academy and in the books of the ancients, that he found the lively and practical training for his future career. There he developed the amazing versatility that was the admiration and despair of other artists. It was at about this time that Verrocchio made for the Medici his famous bronze statue of David, one of his greatest works and perhaps, according to an old tradition, a portrait of his young apprentice from Vinci.

In 1472 Leonardo completed Verrocchio's large picture of *The Baptism of Christ* by painting the head of an angel and a part of the landscape background. Both areas show a subtlety of modeling, and in the landscape there is a feeling for nature which had never been seen in the Western world before. An old story has it that Verrocchio straightway lay down his brushes and turned to sculpture instead, in recognition of the superior talents of his pupil. The fact seems to be, however, that he encouraged Leonardo to take on commissions of his own, and the young man from Vinci was enrolled in the Guild of St. Luke, the guild of the artists, in that same year in acknowledgment of his having achieved mastery in his art. He was twenty years old.

Though we know of a few other paintings done during the next five years or so, the record of his life is very vague, and some think that he may have visited Egypt, Armenia, and the

Taurus Mountains (in what is today Turkey) during that time. This is not nearly so unlikely as it may seem to us today, because Italians were great travelers, and it was a period of exploration. The completeness of the notes that he made on these remote places, along with sketches, suggests firsthand experience, but this remains one of the many mysteries about his life that may never be solved.

Wherever he was in the meantime, by 1480 he had won the patronage of Lorenzo de' Medici, who, only three years older than Leonardo, had inherited the leadership of the city. Thus, still in his twenties, Leonardo was among those who were a part of the Academy which Lorenzo established in the gardens of San Marco, where a brilliant company was assembled. He was recognized as one of the leading artists of that period in Florentine history—which gave Lorenzo the title of the Magnificent—when the city led the world in art and the splendid enjoyment of life. Leonardo became one of a group that included Leon Battista Alberti, pioneer architect of the Renaissance, who wrote discerningly on science and engineering as well as architecture, and was a poet too; Paolo Toscanelli, the greatest cosmographer of the age, sought out by travelers and scholars from all Europe, who first conceived a westward route to the Indies, and is said to have written a letter to the then unknown Columbus in Lisbon in 1474 suggesting the voyage on which, years later, the Genoese explorer embarked; and the merchant-adventurer Amerigo Vespucci, one year Leonardo's senior, who gave his name to the New World. It was such men as these who provided the stimulation in science and technology as well as in art to enable him to develop his extraordinary abilities.

In 1478 Leonardo made a curious and grisly record of an event which shattered the peace of Florence and of all Italy, and changed his life as well as that of Lorenzo de' Medici. It is a sketch of the body of a hanged man, dangling

An Ox and an Ass, c. 1480. Silverpoint and pen. Shortly before starting on his unfinished *Adoration of the Magi* in the Uffizi, Leonardo planned an *Adoration of the Shepherds* for which this is a study. Windsor; reproduced by gracious permission of Her Majesty the Queen

Hanging Body of Bernardo di Bandino Baroncelli, 1478. Pen and ink. Musée Bonnat, Bayonne from a window, one of the murderers of Giuliano de' Medici, Lorenzo's younger brother. Giuliano was murdered in an attempt by the Pazzi family to seize the city. Though the plot failed, it brought on war with Naples and the pope. Lorenzo's diplomacy won over King Ferrante of Naples and created a stalemate—and an uneasy peace. Determined to avoid war, Lorenzo maintained a closer grasp on the affairs of the city than any of his family had before attempted, and he tightened his system of alliances. It was probably for this reason that he urged Leonardo to offer his services to Duke Ludovico of the powerful state of Milan. Lorenzo was confident that Leonardo's abilities would impress and fascinate the duke and thus cement relations between the two cities yet further. Leonardo's letter to the duke lists ten separate capacities, nine of them military, in which he was prepared to serve, proposing to devise "many most powerful machines of war." It is only in the tenth item that he mentions his abilities in painting, sculpture, and architecture and offers to make the equestrian monument of Duke Francesco Sforza, "to the immortal glory and eternal honor of the prince your father of happy memory," which Ludovico had been planning to commission.

Most Illustrious Lord:

Having now sufficiently considered the productions of all those who proclaim themselves skilled contrivers of instruments of war, and having found said instruments in no wise different from those in general use, I venture without prejudice to make known to Your Excellency certain secrets of my own . . . briefly noted as follows:

First: I have a means of making bridges, very light and strong and most easy to carry, with which to pursue or, at other times, flee from the enemy; and also others, proof against fire and indestructible in battle, easily lowered or raised; and I have a method of destroying those of the enemy.

Second: In besieging a place, I know how to drain the water from the moats, and to make an endless variety of bridges, covered ways, scaling ladders, and other machines as might be necessary for such operations.

Third: If, by reason of its elevation or strength, bombardment of a place is impossible, I have a means of destruction of every citadel or stronghold. . . .

Fourth: I know of a kind of light cannon, easy of transport, which hurls a fiery storm, the smoke of which will bring terror to the enemy, to his grave detriment and confusion.

Fifth: By means of secret and tortuous tunnels, dug without noise, I can reach inaccessible places, even if it means passing under a moat or a river.

Sixth: I can make armored vehicles, safe and unattackable, which entering among the enemy with their cannons, there is no body of men so great but they would break them; and behind them the infantry can follow quite without hurt or hindrance.

Seventh: If needed I can make big guns, mortars, and light ordnance in forms both beautiful and useful, and not of the usual type.

Eighth: Where cannon fail, I would construct catapults, mangonels, trabocchi, and other machines of a marvelous efficacy and not in common use. In short, to suit the nature of the case, I can contrive various and endless means of attack or defense.

Ninth: And if the combat were at sea, I have many most powerful machines of war . . . and vessels which withstand the assault of the largest guns and produce flame and smoke.

Tenth: In time of peace I believe I can equal to anyone give perfect satisfaction in architecture, the construction of both public and private buildings, and in the channeling of water from one place to another. Furthermore, the bronze horse may be undertaken, which is to be to the immortal glory and eternal honor of the prince your father of happy memory, and of the illustrious house of Sforza. And if any of the things mentioned above seem impossible or impracticable, I am most ready to make the experiment in your park or whatever place may be chosen by Your Excellency, to whom I commend myself in all humility.

He had a talent not mentioned in his letter which would have made him a welcome addition to any Renaissance court—his outstanding gifts as a musician. He was famous as a composer and an improviser on the lute, and there could have been no present more acceptable to a ruler of the period than that of Lorenzo for the duke, the silver lute "in the shape of a horse's head," which Leonardo had made himself, and on which he could perform with magical ease and grace.

Leonardo's letter tells much about the times and the character of the duke because of its emphasis on war, but it also tells much about Leonardo himself because of its emphasis on technology and engineering. It represents a notable achievement, because his formal education had been that of a poor boy of Florence, mostly in reading and writing and in the use of that instrument typical for the business society of the day, the abacus. The rest he had learned through his experience with Verrocchio, his voracious reading, and his study with the famous mathematician Benedetto d'Abbaco, and with the learned Greek scholar John Agiropoulos, translator of Aristotle into Italian, who had found refuge in Florence after the fall of Constantinople to the Turks in 1453.

While the fashionable circle around Lorenzo was dominated by literary ideas, Leonardo was perfecting himself as a scientist, mathematician, and engineer, as well as an artist. He managed also to read the basic books then available, as his notebooks testify, but where most scholars brought only the experience of the library and the lecture hall to their work, and thus emphasized the theory of ancient authority at the expense of practice and observation, Leonardo brought his whole being. "Anyone who . . . relies upon authority uses not his understanding but his memory," he wrote. "Experience never errs; it is only your judgments that err by promising themselves effects such as are not caused by your experiments." In an age that still revered authority, Leonardo was free to experiment, observe, record, and classify. He was the first to use the modern scientific method.

The Valley of the Arno, 1473. Pen and ink. Inscribed in Leonardo's hand, "the day of the Holy Virgin of the Snows, August 5, 1473," this is his earliest dated drawing, done when he was twenty-one and still working in Verrocchio's shop. Uffizi, Florence

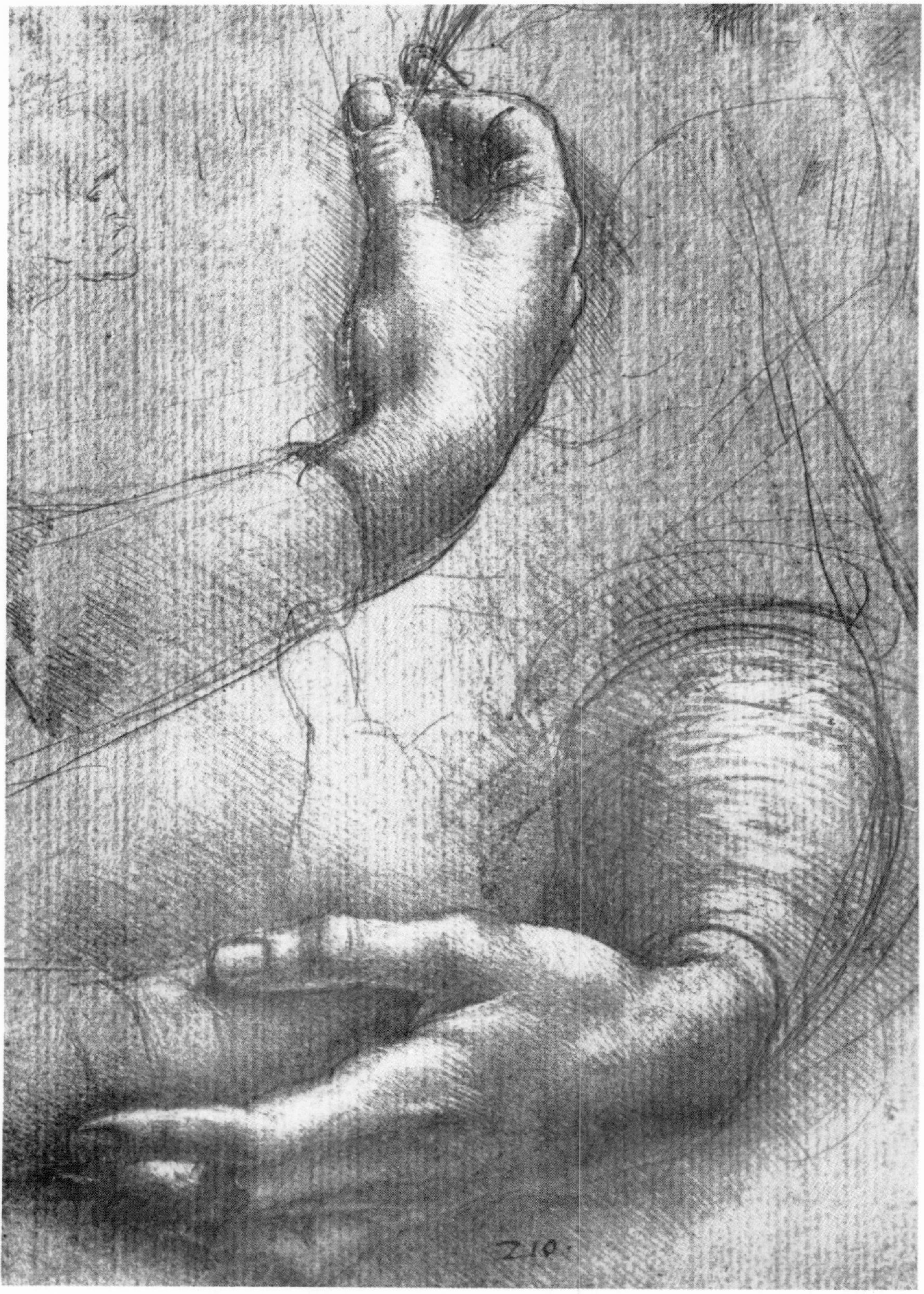

Study of a Woman's Hands, c. 1478–80. Silverpoint heightened with white on pink prepared paper. Windsor; reproduced by gracious permission of Her Majesty the Queen

Profile of a Warrior, c. 1475. Silverpoint on buff prepared paper. This highly finished drawing is based on a lost relief of *Darius* by Verrocchio. The elaborate helmet and cuirass are similar to those produced in Verrocchio's shop for pageants and tournaments staged by the Medici. British Museum, London

LIBRARY
COLBY-SAWYER COLLEGE
NEW LONDON, NH 03257

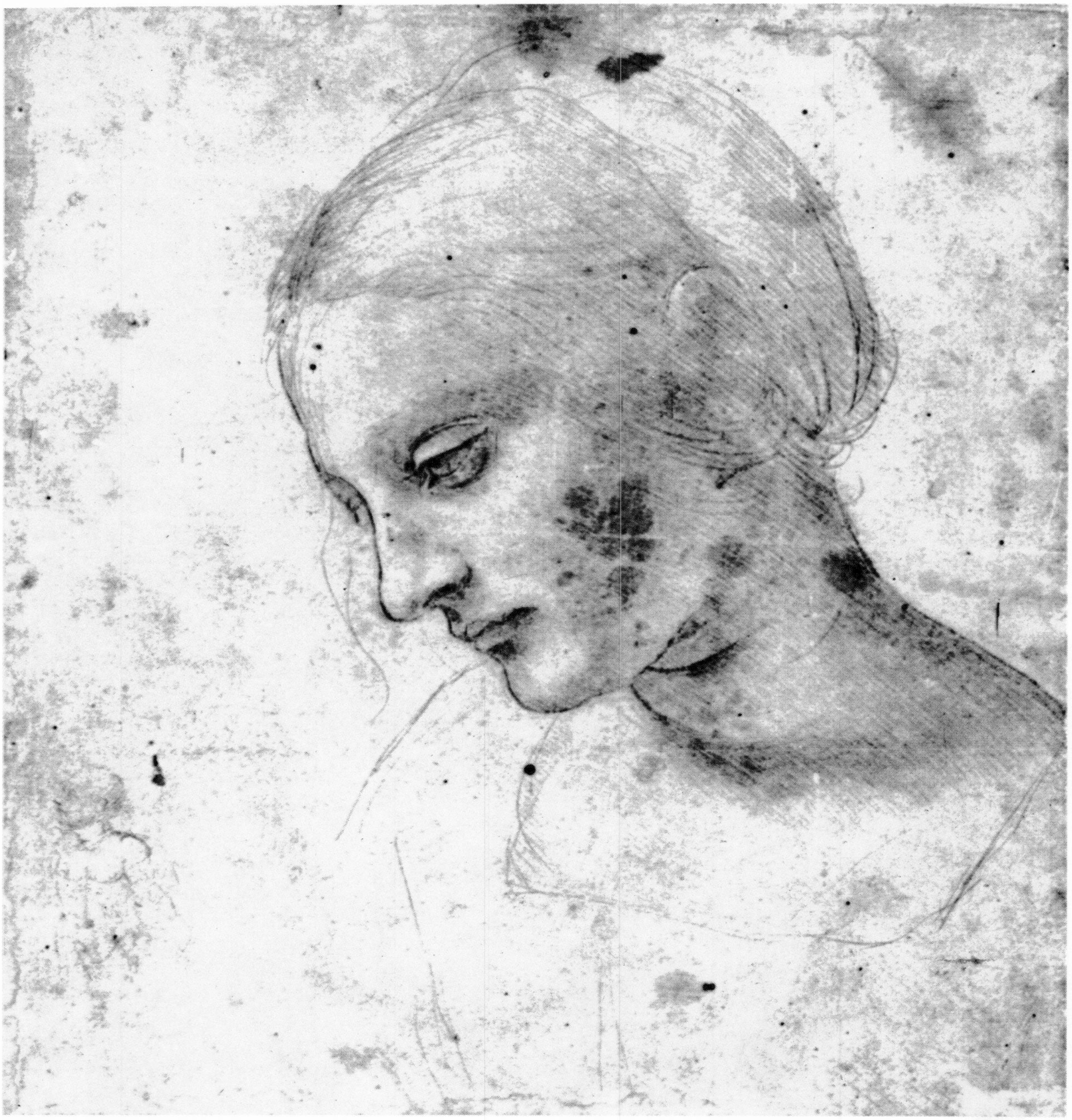

The Head of the Virgin, c. 1480. Silverpoint on greenish paper. A study for a painting the composition of which is known from the *Madonna Litta* in the Hermitage, Leningrad, so damaged and repainted that it is impossible to tell if it is an old copy or the ruin of his original. Louvre, Paris

Angel's Head, c. 1480. Silverpoint on light-brown prepared paper. A study for the angel in *The Virgin of the Rocks* in the Louvre. Royal Library, Turin

At the Court of Ludovico the Moor

It was probably in October of 1482 that Leonardo reached Milan and found a different world from the one he had left in Florence. The city, almost three times larger, was a place of ostentatious wealth. Surrounded by its high walls with their seven gates protected by fifteen battlemented towers rising from the waters of a broad moat, it looked like a great fortress. Built into the massive defenses at the Gate of Jove and rising high above them was the formidable red masonry of the castle of the duke, fortified from both the rest of the city and from the countryside, a reminder that Milan's rulers had often had as much to fear from their own subjects as from a foreign enemy. It was a city of brick, its buildings mostly Gothic because of its nearness to the north, the home of that style which had otherwise taken so little root in Italy. Its cathedral, then the largest in Europe, with its forest of pinnacles, had been designed and built by German craftsmen.

The surrounding countryside was green with wheat and rice fields, orchards, vineyards, and gardens. Mulberry trees had just recently been planted and a silk industry begun which was to become almost as famous as the city's traditional specialty, the manufacture of the finest of arms and armor. On the Street of the Armorers there were more than a hundred shops, constantly busy forging and tempering the matchless steel blades, the pikes, halberds, and lances, and shaping and engraving the elaborate body and horse armor that was used all over Europe. The whole city wore a martial air, from the grim battlements of the duke's castle to the constant presence of armed men, the duke's bodyguard, in the streets. It was a city not of beauty but of power, an expression of its character and violent past. The duchy of which it was the capital extended from the Alps south across the fertile Lombard plain, controlling the land westward to Genoa and eastward to the landward boundaries of the powerful and suspicious republic of Venice. The amazing richness of the soil, the prosperity of its cities, and its geographical position astride the trade and invasion routes through the Alps, gave the region a history of strife and conflict outstanding even in Italy.

Ludovico, called "Il Moro" (the Moor), because of his dark complexion, was the regent but not the duke of Milan when Leonardo became a member of his court. The previous duke had combined a scrupulous observance of religious ritual with a manner of life otherwise so scandalous and vicious that he was assassinated for conduct unbecoming even a Renaissance tyrant. His death left his heir, a small child, to the mercies of his five ambitious brothers. Ludovico, though not the eldest, was the most astute of the five, and had managed to maneuver himself into the position of regent of the duchy and guardian of the child duke. It was a case of setting the fox to watch the chickens, and could have but one eventual outcome. Thus

---

Study for the Sforza Monument, 1488. Silverpoint on blue prepared paper. Windsor; reproduced by gracious permission of Her Majesty the Queen

Ludovico was the actual ruler, though his nephew, a stupid and unhealthy youth, had married and produced an heir, which his uncle had not. This did nothing, however, to change the latter's plans.

Ludovico gathered a brilliant and mixed assemblage of astrologers to assist him in the proper timing of his various schemes, of poets who turned out reams of laudatory verses in heroic style, and of entertainers of all kinds, including the finest musicians in Italy and probably in all Europe at that time. He gloried in the extravagant displays of masques and balls, of processions and concerts, of costume parties where people dressed like characters from ancient myths or from the Middle Ages, with hairy wild men, nymphs, knights, satyrs, and the paladins of Charlemagne mingling with the gods of Olympus. Banquets were so elaborate that the various dishes were creations of wild fantasy, such as roast whole boar garnished with gold leaf, and were sometimes quite inedible though undeniably magnificent. Plates and platters were of silver and gold, and the liveries of the servants of a stunning splendor.

Leonardo was in constant demand to design costumes, to stage plays and tournaments, and to organize musical entertainments, for which he devised various musical instruments and designed an elaborate revolving stage. This was, according to one of Ludovico's guests, a representation of "Paradise formed like an egg which is all gilt in the inside, with a number of lights for the stars, and with niches for the seven planets making a gallant sight. The Paradise resounded with soft music and chants. And so great was the splendor of this marvelous decoration that one at first believed he were seeing the real Paradise." During the performance singers dressed as planets and other celestial deities moved through the air, and Danaë, the maiden loved and then abandoned by Zeus, rose to the sky to become a star, all through the benefit of Leonardo's ingenuity.

Through all these prodigal activities, planned to demonstrate to the world his power and wealth, Ludovico walked watchfully, pursuing his own ambitions, consulting his astrologers and pondering the reports of his secret agents as to the direction of the winds of intrigue in the various courts and capitals of Europe. Apart from the buffoons and pleasure-loving courtiers, he also gathered a group of astute and practical men, engineers, scientists, and military experts. In addition to being master of court revels, Leonardo acted as military and civil engineer, court painter, and started the most ambitious sculptural enterprise of its kind yet attempted, the equestrian statue of Ludovico's father, Duke Francesco Sforza.

In his workshop in one of the courtyards of the castle he made innumerable drawings and clay sketches, and began the laborious task of building up the armature on which to construct the more than life-sized plaster figure of the duke astride a war horse rearing over the prostrate body of a vanquished enemy. He knew the superb mounts in the ducal stables in Milan, considered among the finest in the world. They were of a breed improved and strengthened by stock from Spain, Africa, Arabia, and northern Europe. He studied the wonderful bronze horses of St. Mark, original Greek works from the time of Alexander the Great, which still stand atop the entrance to the cathedral in Venice. They had been brought there years earlier as booty of the victorious Venetian fleet from Constantinople in 1204.

In his drawings for the monument, Leonardo established what his contemporaries greeted as the ideal proportions for the perfect horse. After some trials he discovered that the motive of the rearing charger, never before attempted in history, was too complicated to be practical, as it involved problems in bronze casting which could not be solved with the resources of the day. He began again, and finally a full-scale model, with the horse pacing with the slow dignity befitting the seriousness of a memorial to a great commander, was unveiled to a wondering crowd in the great courtyard of the ducal palace. The unveiling was part of the pageantry celebrating the marriage of Ludovico's niece, Bianca Maria Sforza, to the Emperor Maximilian in November 1493.

An immense store of bronze was collected so

that it could be cast, but Ludovico's turncoat diplomacy and incessant intrigues intensified the threat of war, and the metal was shipped down the River Po to Ferrara, whose duke, his brother-in-law, one of the greatest ordnance experts of the age, made it into cannon. The impressive model remained, however, admired by everyone, until seven years later, when the French captured Milan. It became the target for Gascon archers and was ruined.

Meanwhile, Leonardo had carried out the work for which he became most famous in his lifetime, *The Last Supper,* in the refectory, or dining room, of the Dominican friars at S. Maria delle Grazie. It was finished in 1499, but the masonry of the wall was damp and the artist had used a medium containing oil and varnish. Before he died it was a ruin. What can be seen today, after yet another cleaning in recent years, is the ghost of a profoundly moving work. Though only a trace of the painting remains, it still carries an aura of grandeur, drama, and mystery. It provided an academy of painting for subsequent generations of artists, and the power we can feel in the little that survives is a constant reminder of the greatness of the conception and the tragedy of its loss.

During these years Leonardo was working on the canal system of Lombardy, and on the defenses of the duchy against the French invasion, which seemed imminent. He had mastered Latin and managed to escape from time to time to the duke's great library at nearby Pavia to read works on vision, anatomy, and mathematics. He dissected corpses at the medical school of the university there and pursued the study of perspective with the learned monk Fra Luca Pacioli, another Tuscan. While there he made the greater number of his architectural drawings, including many of domed, centrally

Sketch for *The Last Supper,* c. 1495. Pen and ink. Windsor; reproduced by gracious permission of Her Majesty the Queen

Design for a Stable, c. 1488–89. Pen and ink. Complete with a gravity feed system, this building was intended to house Ludovico's famous horses in ducal splendor. Institut de France, Paris

Study for an Ideal City, c. 1488–89. Pen and ink. The frightening outbreak of the plague in Milan led Leonardo to plan an ideal city with communications, services, and sanitation far in advance of anything actually achieved until modern times. Institut de France, Paris

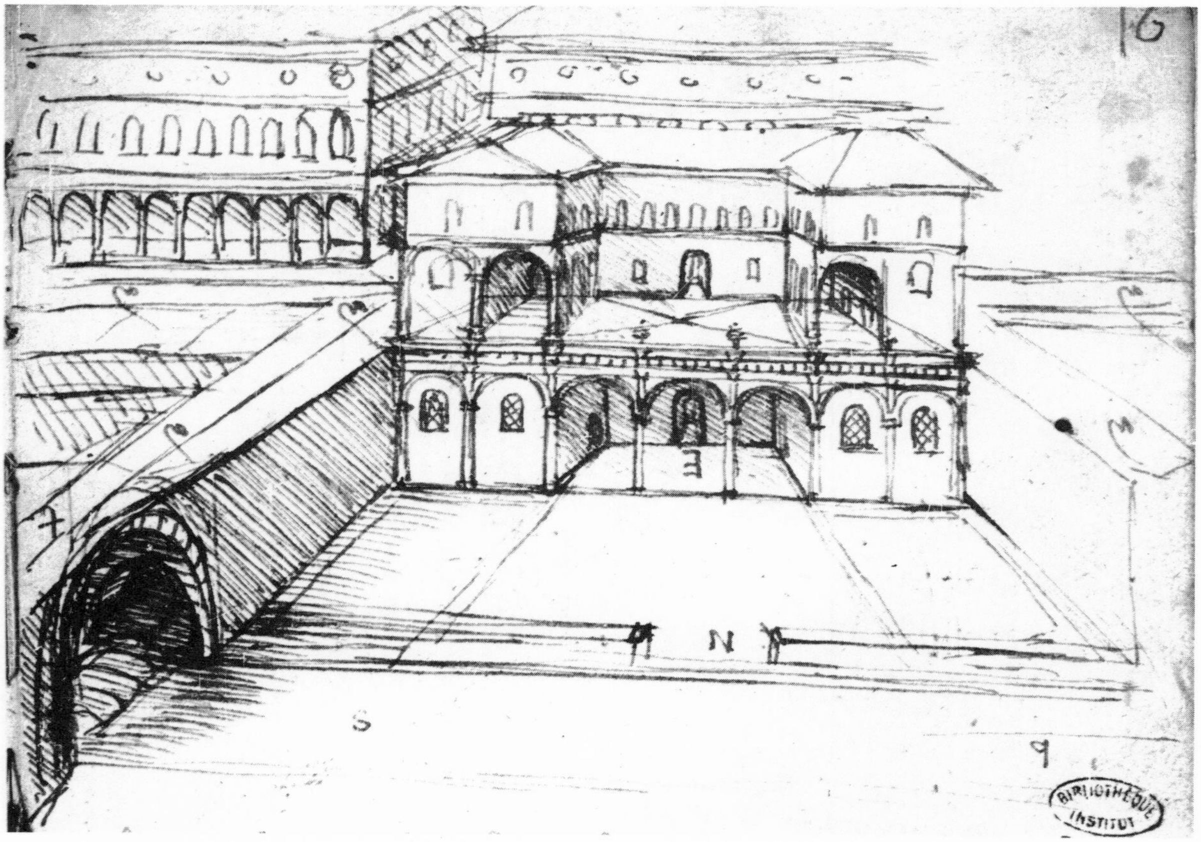

planned churches, which may have influenced his friend Bramante, the great architect, in later choosing a similar concept for St. Peter's in Rome.

He was consulted on the design of a tower for the cathedral of Milan and on the completion of the cathedral of Pavia; in a garden court, he constructed for the duchess a marble bathing pavilion with hot and cold baths; and he designed handsome stables, with a gravity feed system, for the duke's famous horses. Because of a terrifying epidemic of the plague in 1485, he made a series of sketches for an ideal city, without slums and congestion in which disease might flourish. It was complete with upper roadways to be used exclusively by pedestrians, a lower one to be reserved for vehicles. There were spacious plazas and a water and sewage system more sanitary and efficient than any the modern world was to see for many generations.

Meanwhile the political situation was worsening. Louis XII had succeeded to the French throne; his grandfather had been Duke of Milan, and Louis, denouncing Ludovico as a usurper, immediately asserted his claim and formed a league with Venice and the pope. The French Army erupted across the Alps in the summer of 1499, rolled across the fertile plain, taking city after city, and entered Milan that September, while Ludovico sought refuge and assistance from the emperor in the Tyrol. The French viceroy in Milan outraged the people, and in February Ludovico returned with the help of German troops only to be betrayed by his Swiss mercenaries, giving the French an easy victory. As Leonardo succinctly noted, "The duke has lost his state, his possessions, and his liberty, and none of his enterprises has been completed." Ludovico was imprisoned in the stygian darkness of a dungeon far beneath the mighty Château of Loches on the banks of the Indre in the Loire valley from which he was liberated after eight years of solitary confinement only by his death in 1508.

Studies for *The Virgin and Holy Children,* 1482–83. Pen and ink. Here Leonardo is working out a motive which was realized in a lost painting known only through copies, and further developed in *The Virgin of the Rocks* in the Louvre. The Metropolitan Museum, New York

Studies of Flowers, c. 1483. Pen and ink over metal-point. Academy, Venice

Studies of Horses for the Sforza Monument, c. 1488. Pen and ink over black chalk. Windsor; reproduced by gracious permission of Her Majesty the Queen

Designs for a Domed Church, 1488–89. Pen and ink. Institut de France, Paris

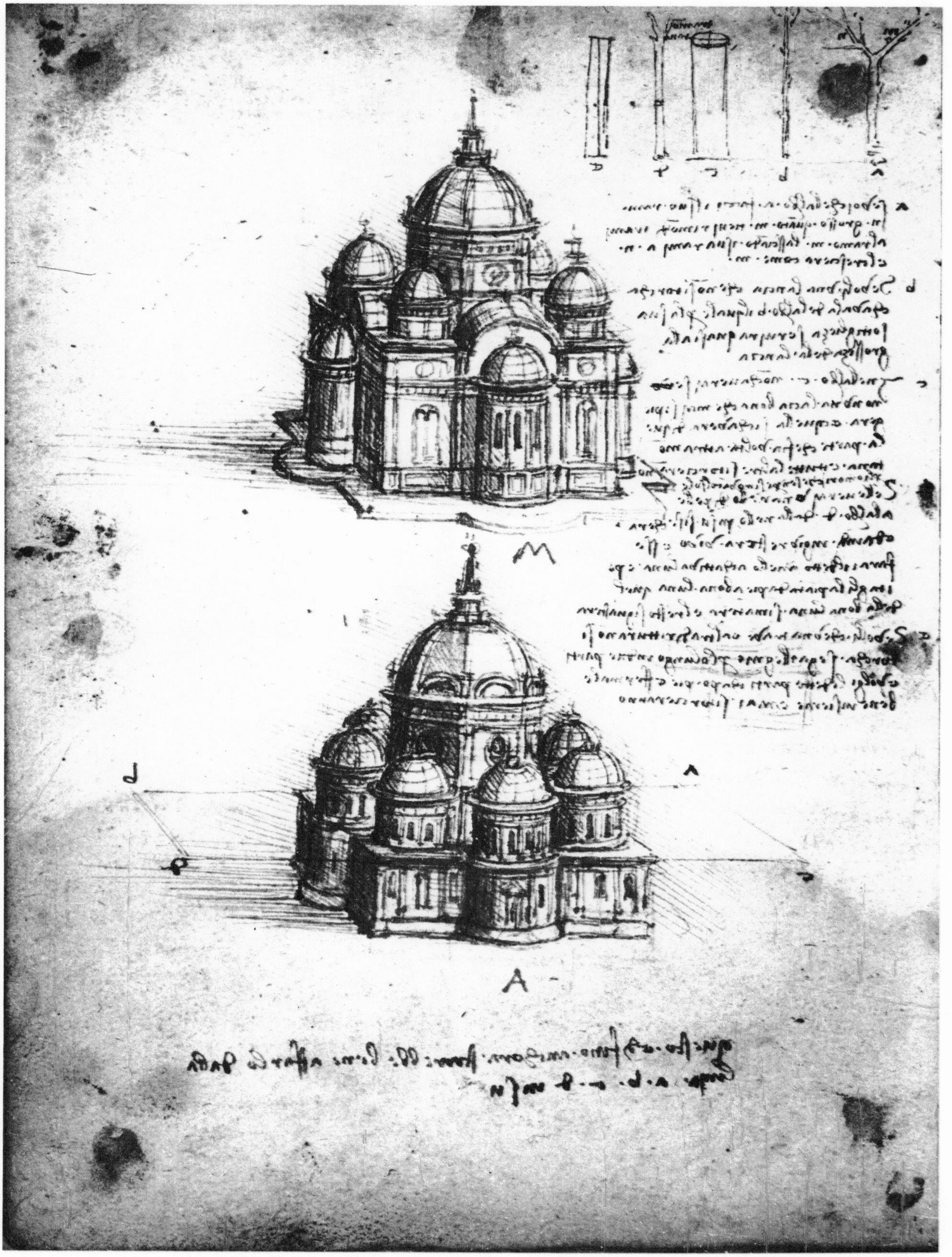

A Study from Nature for the Sforza Monument, 1490. Silverpoint on blue prepared paper. Windsor; reproduced by gracious permission of Her Majesty the Queen

Study for St. James the Greater in *The Last Supper,* 1495–96. Red chalk. The sketch in pen and ink at the lower left may be of battlements of the Sforza Castle at Milan. Windsor; reproduced by gracious permission of Her Majesty the Queen

44

PAGES 48–49: Study for *The Last Supper,* 1495–97. Red chalk. The apostles in the lower range continue the upper group to the left. Academy, Venice

The Unsettled Years

In Milan the confusion of war mounted, and toward Christmas of 1499 Leonardo and Fra Luca Pacioli went to Venice. Built on sandbars off the northern Adriatic coast by refugees from the terrors of Attila and the Huns in 451, the ancient city had become a republic and the world's greatest center of trade with the East. There was something oriental in the character of the state, whose power lay in the hands of a few ancient and noble families, so jealous of their control that they surrounded their elected duke with informers, regarded any change with suspicion, and allotted a large percentage of the city's annual revenue to the consistent and judicious bribery of kings and prelates, generals and pirates, whom they also kept track of through their own spies as an added precaution.

Today the city dreams, but then it was a scene of canals crowded with gondolas, of the pageantry of frequent processions, of squares full of activity. There were merchants and statesmen, peddlers and priests, princes and courtesans, children and dogs. On the waterfront, thronged with ships, sailors, and stevedores, one could hear all the tongues of East and West.

Venice was at war with the Turks, and Leonardo was even more welcome as a military engineer than as an artist. The Doge and Council consulted him about the defenses of the eastern boundaries toward Trieste. He studied the situation and recommended that certain low-lying, strategically located areas of the country be flooded to impede invaders. And he advised taking the offensive against the Grand Turk, the Sultan Bajazet II, with a submarine attack on the Turkish Navy, and the sinking of enemy vessels by divers equipped to bore holes in the ships from beneath the water.

Before the end of April 1500 he was back in Florence after an absence of almost twenty years. He had been wise in deciding not to return to Milan. His good friend, the architect Giacomo da Ferrara had gone back only to be hanged, drawn, and quartered by the French commander for having been a supporter of Il Moro. Leonardo had prudently transferred funds to a Florentine bank before leaving Milan.

He found the city radically changed. Lorenzo the Magnificent was long since forgotten, the Medici banished, and the government an uneasy republic. The first work he did, a cartoon for an altarpiece, "not only filled all artists with wonder," Vasari wrote in his famous *Lives of the Artists,* "but, when it was finished men and women, young and old, continued for two days to crowd into the room where it was exhibited, as if attending a solemn festival; and all were astonished at its excellence." Florence might have changed but the old enthusiasm for the arts was still there. Leonardo was stimulated by it, but he pursued his scientific studies as well, and in 1502 made a move which seems today almost incomprehensible. He entered the service as a military engineer of the notorious Cesare Borgia, the son of Pope Alexander VI.

It was Cesare Borgia who revived the old idea of the unification of Italy, but under Borgia rule. After murdering his brother, the Duke of

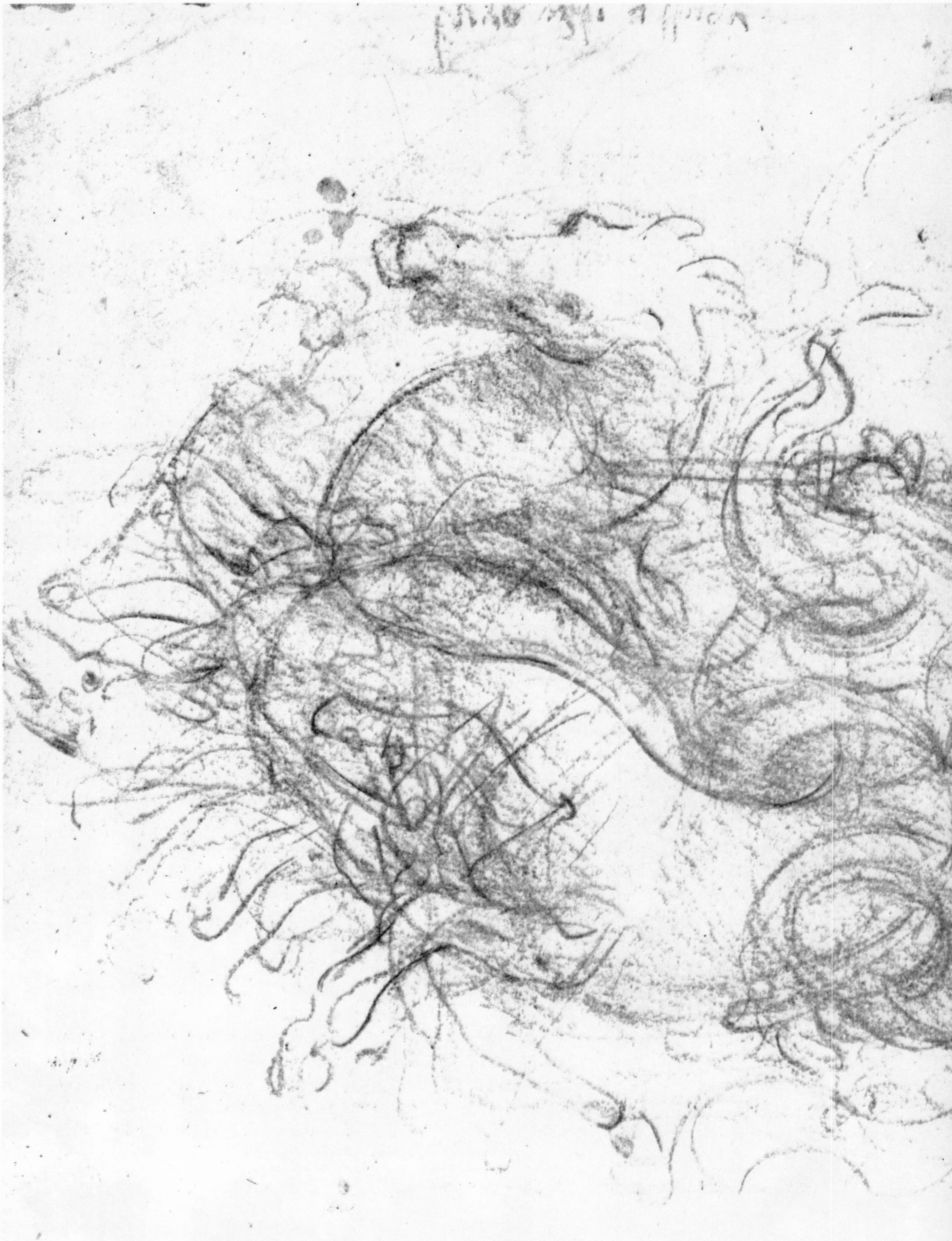

Gandia, and tossing his body into the Tiber, Cesare was appointed captain-general of the armies of the church. He then set out to achieve his purpose through his favorite methods of treachery, murder, torture, and rapine to a degree that established some sort of all-time record for perfidy during a period that maintained an extraordinarily high standard in such lamentable achievements. His ambition was so boundless and his thirst for power so intense that his criminal insanity seems obvious from the vantage point of today. Yet there was a harsh and theatrical brightness to his unbelievable performance that commanded attention in a period that had newly rediscovered individualism and consequently tended to admire even its wildest manifestations. Leonardo made a remarkable drawing of the head of Cesare from three angles, with all the dispassionate objectivity of his anatomical studies, but it shows neither the light of obsessive madness in the eyes nor the running

---

PAGES 52–53: Neptune in his Chariot, 1504. Black chalk. A study for a highly finished drawing, now lost, that Leonardo made for his friend Antonio Segni, a connoisseur and collector. Windsor; reproduced by gracious permission of Her Majesty the Queen

Fighting Horsemen, 1503–4. Pen and ink. A study for the lost fresco of *The Battle of Anghiari*. Academy, Venice

sores disfiguring the face that were soon to become so frighteningly obvious that he wore a black mask and went abroad only after dark.

During this brief period Leonardo led a life of extreme activity which came to a stop shortly after his friend Vitelli, one of the least reprehensible of the generals in Borgia employ, was strangled at Cesare's order. Leonardo had been given a commission as chief architect and engineer of the papal forces with absolute authority to requisition anything needed to carry out his function. But his commission became meaningless when the period of Cesare's power suddenly ended with the death of Alexander VI and the succession of a warrior who loved the field of battle, a nephew of Sixtus IV, as Pope Julius II. As Cesare's star sank in madness and disease, that of Julius' rose in splendor. His was one of the most significant reigns of the Renaissance, made glorious by his patronage of almost all the great artists and architects of the time. It was he who conceived the idea of rebuilding St. Peter's, thus having a key part in the creation of one of the noblest monuments in the world. The diabolical shadow of the Borgias, which had been cast not only across Italy but all Christendom as well, vanished in the new light.

Back again in Florence, Leonardo was busy painting perhaps the most famous portrait in the world, the *Mona Lisa,* today the great treasure of the Louvre in Paris. We can no longer see her as Leonardo painted her; the colors have darkened beneath layers of varnish, and the figure seems enveloped in the shadows in which the picture hangs. Yet we can make out the strange and distant moonscape in the background, a further expression of the same mystery which all his life Leonardo sought to penetrate.

He was also active as an engineer and surveyor, and, at the request of the government of Florence, undertook, for the Council Chamber, a mural painting of an event famous in Florentine history. Michelangelo, the other leading Florentine artist, was given a similar commission, and chose *The Battle of Cascina,* an episode in which a group of soldiers, while swimming in a river, were surprised by the enemy. This gave the artist an opportunity to form a composition of the heroic nude male figures for which he was so famous. Leonardo selected *The Battle of Anghiari,* an action in which the cavalry figured prominently, thus enabling him to produce a swirling group of horses and riders in wild combat. One can imagine the keen interest with which the Florentines watched this contest of the champions. Curiously, neither work was completed, yet both were so widely esteemed that they influenced artists for generations to come. Both cartoons were literally worn out from admiring study, and the compositions are known to us only through copies.

In 1506 Charles d'Amboise, the Lord of Chaumont and the French governor of Milan, asked the Florentine government to allow Leonardo to return to the north to carry out an urgent commission. No one knows today what that commission was, but he went, leaving the *Anghiari* fresco unfinished, and at the order of Louis XII stayed to carry out various works for the French King, who spoke often of "the perfection and other qualities of Leonardo." He traveled much, especially in the Alps, where he found in the rock the fossilized skeleton of a great fish that, "destroyed by Time," he wrote, "is become an armour and support to the mountain which lies above it." He had a final opportunity to return to the project of an equestrian statue, a commission for Gian Giacomo Trivulzio, the general who succeeded d'Amboise as French governor of Milan. Many drawings for it remain, along with sketches for a palace for the same patron, but again politics intervened and the project came to nothing. The rule of the duchy passed to the Spaniards, with an alliance of Venetians and papal mercenaries.

Milan was in decline, and late in 1513 Leonardo went to Rome under the patronage of Giuliano de' Medici, Duc de Nemours, son of Lorenzo the Magnificent and brother of Giovanni de' Medici, who had been elected pope as Leo X in that year. A cardinal at thirteen and pope at thirty-seven, Leo had none of the forthright vigor of his predecessor, Julius II, who did not hesitate to climb the scaffold to belabor

Michelangelo with his cane in an effort to make him complete the Sistine frescoes more quickly, an attempt which the latter successfully combatted by the simple expedient of a work strike. Instead, Leo X, with a genuine passion for the arts, vigorously carried forward the construction of the new St. Peter's, collected ancient gems and manuscripts and all sorts of works of art which are today a part of the wonderful Vatican collections, and encouraged all the creative world of Italy and beyond to come to Rome.

Thus Leonardo, at sixty-one, found himself surrounded by a large group of painters, sculptors, craftsmen, and architects, most of whom were scheming and competing for the pope's attention. The outstanding leaders were well established in official favor. Raphael, at thirty-one, was at work on his famous frescoes in the papal palace, and Michelangelo, at thirty-nine, had just completed, after more than three cramped and uncomfortable years spent on the scaffold, the epic paintings of *The Creation* and *The Fall of Man* on the ceiling of the Sistine Chapel.

At Giuliano's request Leonardo was lodged in rooms in the Belvedere Palace and assigned assistants, who unfortunately proved incompe-

Dragons. Silverpoint and some pen and ink on white prepared paper. Windsor; reproduced by gracious permission of Her Majesty the Queen

tent and dishonest. Jealous rivals made his life miserable and their false reports led to the pope's forbidding his anatomical dissections. He buried himself in his work, and to discourage interruptions he kept a tame lizard of unusual variety, which one of the Vatican gardeners had found and given him. He made a pair of glistening wings for it, and fantastic horns, a beard, and brilliant false eyes set above its own, all attached with a harmless adhesive of his own devising. Superstitious visitors were terrified when it ran shimmering across the floor and up the walls looking like a small dragon, its wings quivering as if it were about to fly.

In 1515 Guiliano, Duc de Nemours, as papal commander, accompanied the pope to Bologna for a secret conference with Francis I, who had just succeeded to the throne of France, and Leonardo may have gone along with his patron. When, in the following year, Giuliano died at thirty-seven, Leonardo was free to accept the invitation of the king to come to his court. So in 1516 he packed his precious notebooks, his portfolios of drawings, paintings, and other possessions for the last time, and set out on a journey across the Alps to become in his old age "First Painter and Engineer to the King of France."

King Francis lived much of each year at the Château of Amboise on the Loire, and gave Leonardo a handsome house nearby, the Manor

122

of Cloux. Leonardo laid out a canal system for that part of the river valley, and planned a palace and a model town at Romorantin, where the king had spent his boyhood. He continued his scientific studies and staged special events for the court. He devised a mechanical lion that took several steps forward as if to attack the king, and then opened up to display the gleaming white lilies of France against a vivid blue background. And in the spring of 1518, in celebration of the baptism of the dauphin and the wedding of the king's niece to Lorenzo de' Medici, Duke of Urbino and another brother of Leo X, a ball was held in the courtyard at Cloux, with decorations and entertainments designed by Leonardo himself. In the meantime, the king visited him almost daily to enjoy his conversation and ask his advice. As Francis told the famous Florentine goldsmith, Benvenuto Cellini, almost twenty years later, "No other man had been born who had attained such great knowledge as Leonardo, and not only as sculptor, painter, and architect, for beyond that he was a profound philosopher."

A Dog. Red chalk. The model for this drawing appears several times among Leonardo's sketches and was probably a member of his household. Windsor; reproduced by gracious permission of Her Majesty the Queen

Spray of a Plant, c. 1505–8. Red chalk touched with white on pink prepared paper. Windsor; reproduced by gracious permission of Her Majesty the Queen

Portrait Sketch of Cesare Borgia from Three Sides, 1502. Red chalk. Royal Library, Turin

Studies for *St. George and the Dragon,* 1507–8. Pen and ink over black chalk. Windsor; reproduced by gracious permission of Her Majesty the Queen

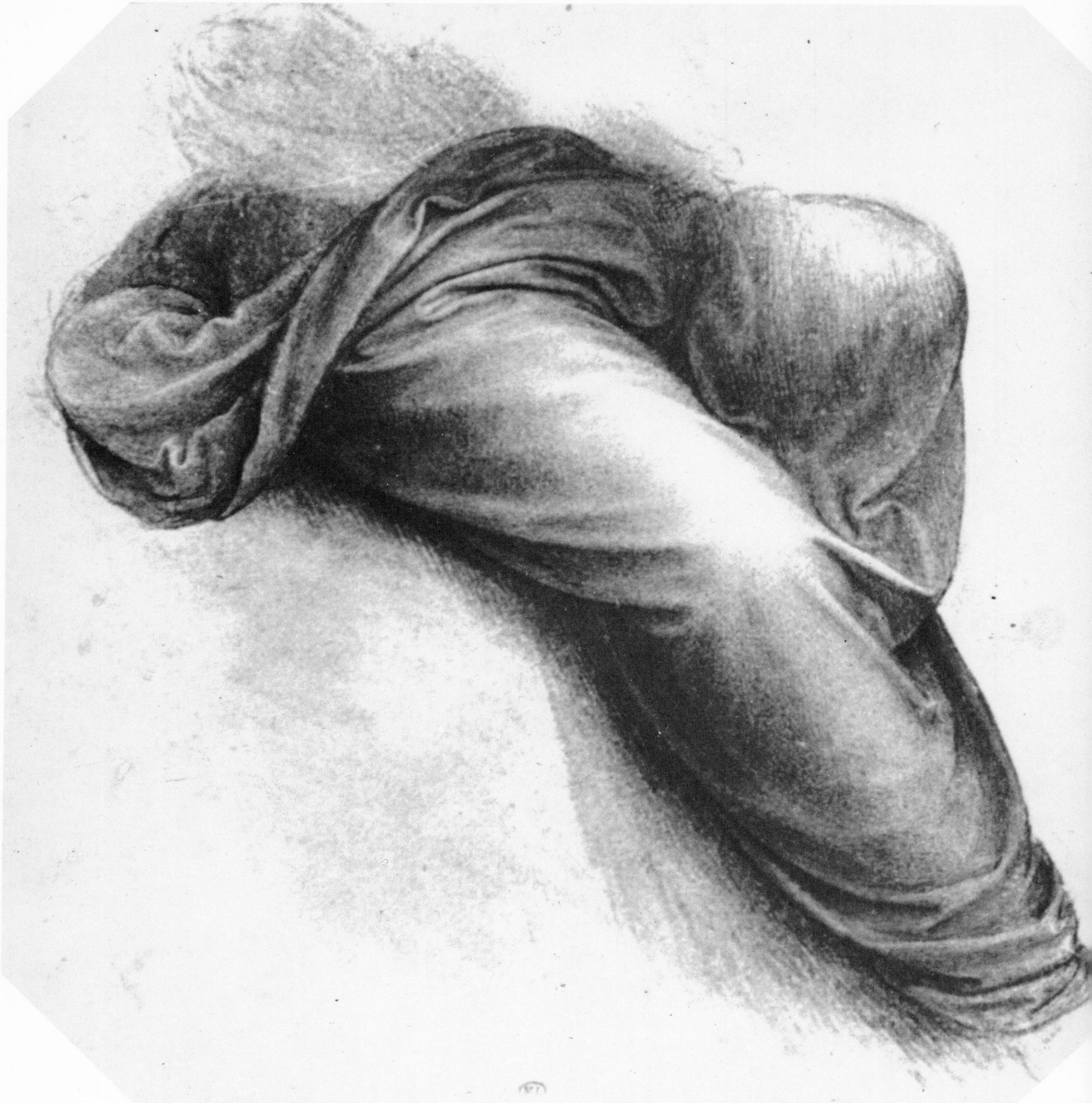

Study of Drapery for *The Madonna and Child with St. Anne,* c. 1501. Black chalk, india ink wash, touched with white. Both the finished painting and this drawing are in the Louvre, Paris

Studies for the Equestrian Monument of Gian Giacomo Trivulzio, 1511–12. Pen and bister on gray paper. Trivulzio was the governor of Milan for the French after the defeat of Ludovico il Moro in 1499. The marble base of the bronze horseman was to contain a sarcophagus and be guarded by four bronze figures at the corners. Windsor; reproduced by gracious permission of Her Majesty the Queen

Masquerader in Costume, c. 1513. Black chalk. Windsor; reproduced by gracious permission of Her Majesty the Queen

A Sketch of Amboise, c. 1516. Red chalk. King Francis I's favorite château was here, and Leonardo spent his last years at the Manor of Cloux nearby. Windsor; reproduced by gracious permission of Her Majesty the Queen

II

"I Wish to Work Miracles"

"The Air Is Filled with Countless Images"

Leonardo was known by his contemporaries to have been gifted with the exceptional quickness of eye and reaction found only occasionally among great athletes, and it proved an invaluable asset in science as well as in art. For him the eye was the key to everything. Of the pupil of the eye he wrote, "Who would believe that so small a space could contain the images of all the universe. O mighty process! What talent can avail to penetrate so great a wonder? . . . These are the miracles . . ." Fascinated by the problems of vision, he experimented with lenses, and designed a device perhaps intended as a sort of searchlight but interpreted by many as a projector, an ancestor of the modern slide projector and rather like an old-fashioned magic lantern.

Among his many notes on astronomical subjects is the reminder to "make glasses in order to see the moon large." Many were working with lenses at this time. Leonardo was undoubtedly aware of the clearer view possible through their use, not only of the moon and stars, but also of minute objects as well. Two centuries before Isaac Newton, he had learned the secret of making bronze as hard and close-grained, and also as brittle, as glass, but as capable of being as highly polished, and thus ideal for magnifying mirrors. When preparing the bell metal, "put burnt copper into the mixture," he advised, "or corrupt it with arsenic, but it will be brittle."

He designed machines to grind both mirrors and lenses with a focal length appropriate only for purposes of astronomical observation. This fact and the evidence of the many diagrams and references to observations throughout his notes have led several authorities to conclude that Leonardo made a telescope in a simple form about 1492, and a more advanced one, with a concave mirror replacing the convex lens, in 1508. Soon after, both the telescope and the microscope were to be at the service of the scientist, and a new age of science, of which he was the pioneer, was to dawn.

Visual appearance and visual analysis played an important part in all of Leonardo's work, from the amazing subtlety of modeling in his paintings to the split-second, action-stopping poses in some of his drawings. It was natural, therefore, that he should have been much interested in the newly developed theory of perspective which, for the first time in history, reduced the process of visual representation to scientific principles.

During the Middle Ages man's attention was directed away from the things of this earth, which the church taught was merely an imperfect shadow of the next world, glorious and permanent. The arts tended understandably to be otherworldly, paying less attention to appearances than to the expression of spiritual values and faith in the eternal life to come.

A woodcut illustration, the drawing for which was done by Leonardo, for Pacioli's book on perspective, *The Divine Proportion,* published in Venice in 1509

During the Renaissance a significant change came with man's sudden rediscovery of the world around him. With that change came a different way of looking at things. It was appropriate that Filippo Brunelleschi, first great architect of the Renaissance and designer of the dome of the cathedral of Florence, was the first to conceive of a painting as a window through which to see the real world rather than, as in the Middle Ages, and again in our own day, a plain opaque surface upon which symbolic images are painted. The difference between the two concepts is profound. In the Renaissance the artist and the scientist became one in a pioneering investigation in seeing and realizing the three-dimensional space in which man lives and works. Their discoveries became man's idea of reality, to remain virtually unchallenged until our own day when the infinitesimal world of the atom and the incomprehensible vastness of space have combined to shatter the neatness and clarity of the Renaissance idea, much as the Copernican system destroyed the reassuring understandability of Aristotle's harmonious spheres.

Leonardo likened the surface of a picture to "a pane of glass," and suggested the use of the sort of apparatus later constructed by the famous German Renaissance artist, his younger contemporary, Albrecht Dürer, in which a glass plate is held vertically on a stand, with a guide for the painter's eye so that he cannot, by moving about, distort the image which he traces on the glass and then transfers exactly to his panel. Such a device was widely used, especially by portrait painters, for several centuries thereafter.

In the meantime Leonardo made the illustrations for the famous book on perspective, *The Divine Proportion,* whose very title implies the importance attached to the subject. It was written in Milan by his friend Fra Luca Pacioli, and published in Venice in 1509. The mere description of the apparatus Leonardo suggested and Dürer constructed reveals the principles of the system that Brunelleschi invented, the idea that the artist records the exact places where the invisible rays, or lines, connecting his eye with the objects to be represented intersect the plane of the picture. He conceived of a vanishing point where all lines, like railroad tracks across a plain, appear to converge. Thus he could express relations in depth by proportionate re-

Landscape with a River and a Canal, c. 1503. Pen and ink. Windsor; reproduced by gracious permission of Her Majesty the Queen

duction in size with the increase of distance from the viewer.

The new command of space ensured by the science of perspective made possible not only Renaissance painting, but architectural concepts on a grand scale, such as town and city planning, illusionistic stage sets like those designed by Leonardo for the ducal court at Milan and for Francis I, the making of maps and charts so important for the explorers of the period, and the accurate and understandable illustration of data so necessary for progress in virtually every scientific field from astronomy to anatomy. The practice of perspective also employed principles of geometry and thus led to further developments vital for the advancement of science in general.

Leonardo developed a superb system of graphic description in connection with his anatomical studies, which he also used to great advantage in mechanical and other drawings. "You who think to reveal the figure of a man in words," he wrote, "with his limbs arranged in all their different attitudes, banish the idea from you, for the more minute your description, the more you will confuse the mind of the reader and the more you will lead him away from the knowledge of the thing described."

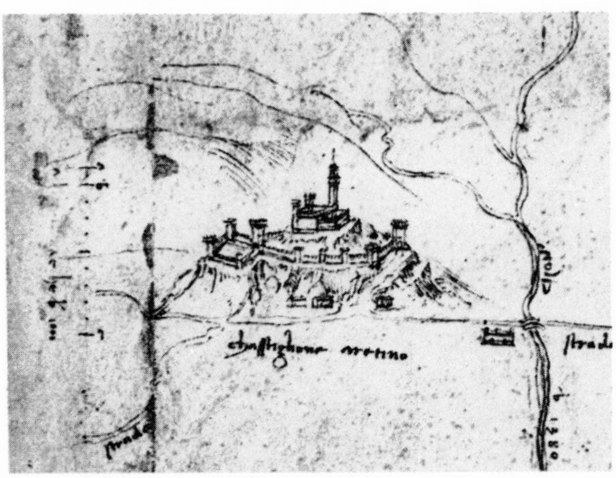

Bird's-eye View of a Castle from a Map of the Arezzo Area. Ambrosiana, Milan

He also proved the superiority for study of drawings over actual dissections, pointing out that it was necessary to make many dissections on a series of different bodies to discover the complete form and function of each part. These must be examined "from different aspects, from below, from above and from the sides. . . . Therefore by my plan you will become acquainted with every part and every whole by means of a demonstration of each part from three different aspects."

The science of perspective made possible this full recording, with an accurate third dimension, demanded by scientific precision. He drew cross sections with precise measurements, better to express the structure and form of various parts, often separating the sections for clarity. Here was born not only a science of anatomy, but also the means of graphic representation basic

Anatomy of a Leg in Exploded Sections. Pen and ink. Windsor; reproduced by gracious permission of Her Majesty the Queen

to modern high-speed production, depending as it must on production illustrations and exploded drawings. It needed only the addition of orthogonal projection for the applied descriptive geometry of mechanical drawing to be developed. This is a three-dimensional system of drawing in which there is no diminution of size and scale with depth, and all projection lines are either parallel or perpendicular to each other. Orthogonal projection is the contribution of a French scientist of the late eighteenth century, Gaspard Monge.

Today the two systems, the perspective and the orthogonal, along with multiview drawings, are used together to achieve the clarity and completeness demanded by modern technology. Thus, amazingly, the perspective developments of Brunelleschi, Alberti, Pacioli, and Leonardo in the fifteenth century have, as one expert has pointed out, an influence on the production of spacecraft in the twentieth.

Leonardo was fascinated with human proportions, which he endeavored to establish according to an ideal system, much as his studies for the Sforza monument had done for those of horses. He went into the utmost detail in the minuteness of his descriptions of the proportions of the body, and obviously based his precepts on the tabulated measurements of many individuals. "The distance from the attachment of one ear to the other is equal to that from the meeting of the eyebrows to chin," he wrote, "and in a fine face the width of the mouth is equal to the length from the parting of the lips to the bottom of the chin." He goes on to describe the entire body in similar terms of relative proportions down to "space between the extreme poles inside and outside the foot called the ankle or anklebone," which, he tells us, is "equal to the space between the mouth and the inner corner of the eye." All this careful system was, of course, useful for artists, but it also led into studies of far-reaching scientific consequence.

Galen, the Greek physician of the second century, whose works were medical textbooks for the Middle Ages and the Renaissance, had never performed a dissection of a human body. This vital area of scientific research remained virtually closed to investigators because of the Christian abhorrence at disturbing the remains of the dead, no matter what barbarities were committed on the living. But at Padua, the greatest center of medicine in the world for several centuries, a public dissection took place in 1341. Others followed, but in a fashion scarcely calculated to enlighten the aspiring medical students, since the knife was handled by a menial assistant while the professor read appropriate passages from Galen, whether they agreed with the evidence of the demonstration or not.

Though medicine may have been reluctantly satisfied with such an unreal approach, art was not. Artists began their own investigations of the bones and muscles, as opposed to the intestines (which, perhaps understandably, preoccupied the physicians) until medical students are recorded as having studied the figures painted by artists, since they could learn more from them than they could in class. Thus there were a number of painters, including Michelangelo, who were anatomists as well as artists. Leonardo, however, belonged to a different category: he was the first artist, not just to study the body to perfect his art, but to place his art at the service of science and invent thereby a new means of analytical study and record, the science of anatomy. And because he dissected animals as well as humans to consider similarities and differences in organs, tissues, muscles, and bone structures, he was a pioneer in comparative anatomy as well.

Leonardo's achievements in this field were the result not only of his keen observation and his development of a system of visual recording, but also of bringing other artistic techniques to anatomical research. For example, he used his knowledge as a sculptor to determine for the first time in history the form of the human brain. He did it by draining the cranial cavities of a skull and filling them with wax, using, as in casting a bronze, two little tubes to allow the air to escape. After the wax had hardened, he had a perfect mold of the brain from which to cast a model. He could then make as many sections of it as he wished to reveal the complexities of its contour. This method of wax injection was thereafter used by anatomists from the seventeenth century to our own day.

People used to think that, because Leonardo's works remained in manuscript, they were without influence on the course of scientific development, and that this represented one of the great losses in human history. Quite clearly, such a conclusion is far from the truth. During his period the publication of scientific treatises was most exceptional, and engineers' drawings of the time are proof that their graphic skills were not sufficiently developed to illustrate mechanical ideas. The passing on of technical and professional knowledge was personal, from expert to expert and from master to pupil. As in earlier periods, works circulated in manuscript. The great art historian Irwin Panofsky has emphasized that "a number of anatomical drawings by Leonardo were copied by Dürer . . ." and discovered that "a considerable number of other scientific drawings . . . are known to us through North Italian copies of the latter half of the Sixteenth Century." After Leonardo's death his notebooks were seen and studied by many, including the talented and unscrupulous Milanese mathematician Girolamo Cardano, who pirated a greater part of his work in mechanical science and published the borrowings in two treatises which gave Leonardo's ideas great currency without acknowledgment to him.

Others of the manuscripts were stolen, and many were copied, so his influence was a continuing one. While still in Milan he participated in 1510 and 1511 in a series of dissections with the much younger Marc Antonio dalla Torre, who came from a family of physicians from Verona. The leading anatomist of his generation, dalla Torre was a professor at the universities of Pavia and Padua, where two decades later his successor Andreas Vesalius began his great work, *The Structure of the Human Body,* magnificently illustrated with woodcuts by a pupil of Titian, and published at Basle in 1543. The most monumental achievement of its kind, it embodied not only material derived from Leonardo but also his basic scientific approach, which thus passed into the mainstream of the world's knowledge.

Composition Sketch for *The Adoration of the Magi,* 1481. Pen and ink over metalpoint. Leonardo here combines the elements he planned to use in the painting: the sense of adoration conveyed by the kneeling figures and contrasted to the standing philosopher in meditation, and the architectural setting of a ruined palace courtyard with stairs and many figures. The drawing's uncertainty and incompleteness record the evolution of the composition in his mind even as his pen gropes to express his ideas. In the completed composition his mastery of perspective was to integrate these elements into a dramatic whole. Louvre, Paris

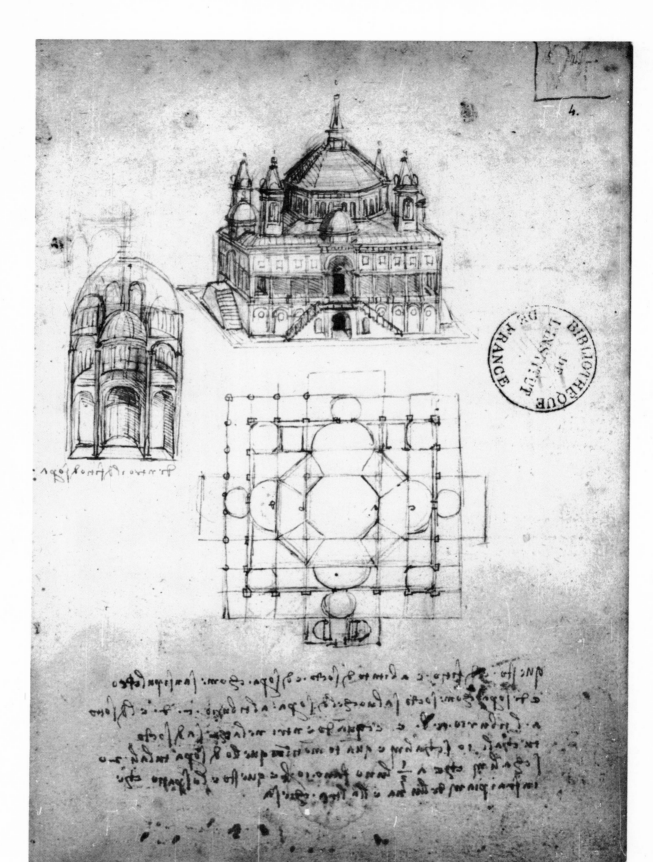

BIBLIOTHÈQUE DE L'INSTITUT DE FRANCE

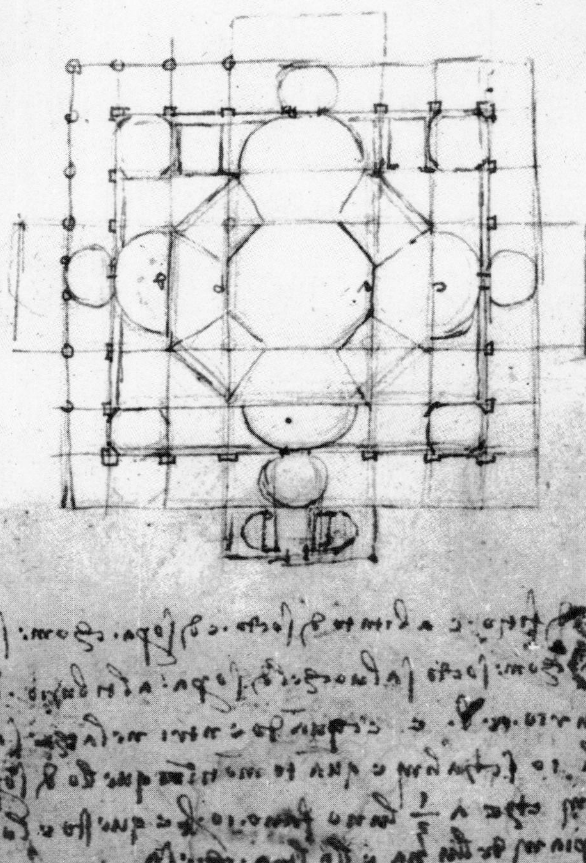

A Square Church with Dome and Minarets, c. 1488–89. Pen and ink. At the bottom of the sheet Leonardo wrote, "This building is usable both below and above, like San Sepolcro, and is the same above as below, except that the upper story has the dome *c d,* and the lower has the dome *a b*. And when you enter the crypt you descend ten steps, and when you ascend to the upper you climb twenty steps, which, with one third *braccio* for each makes ten *braccia*. This is the height between one floor of the church and the other." The Florentine *braccio* as used by architects was twenty-three inches. The science of perspective both encouraged and made possible such highly organized architectural concepts in terms of complex spatial relationships. Bibliothèque Nationale, Paris

Studies of Mountain Ranges, c. 1511. Red chalk on red prepared paper, touched with white. "The dark colors of the shadows of mountains at a great distance take a more beautiful and purer blue than those parts which are in light," Leonardo noted. He observed the effect of light and atmosphere from the upper slopes of Monte Rosa, "a peak of the Alps which divide France from Italy," and made notes on aerial perspective for his unfinished treatise on painting. Windsor; reproduced by gracious permission of Her Majesty the Queen

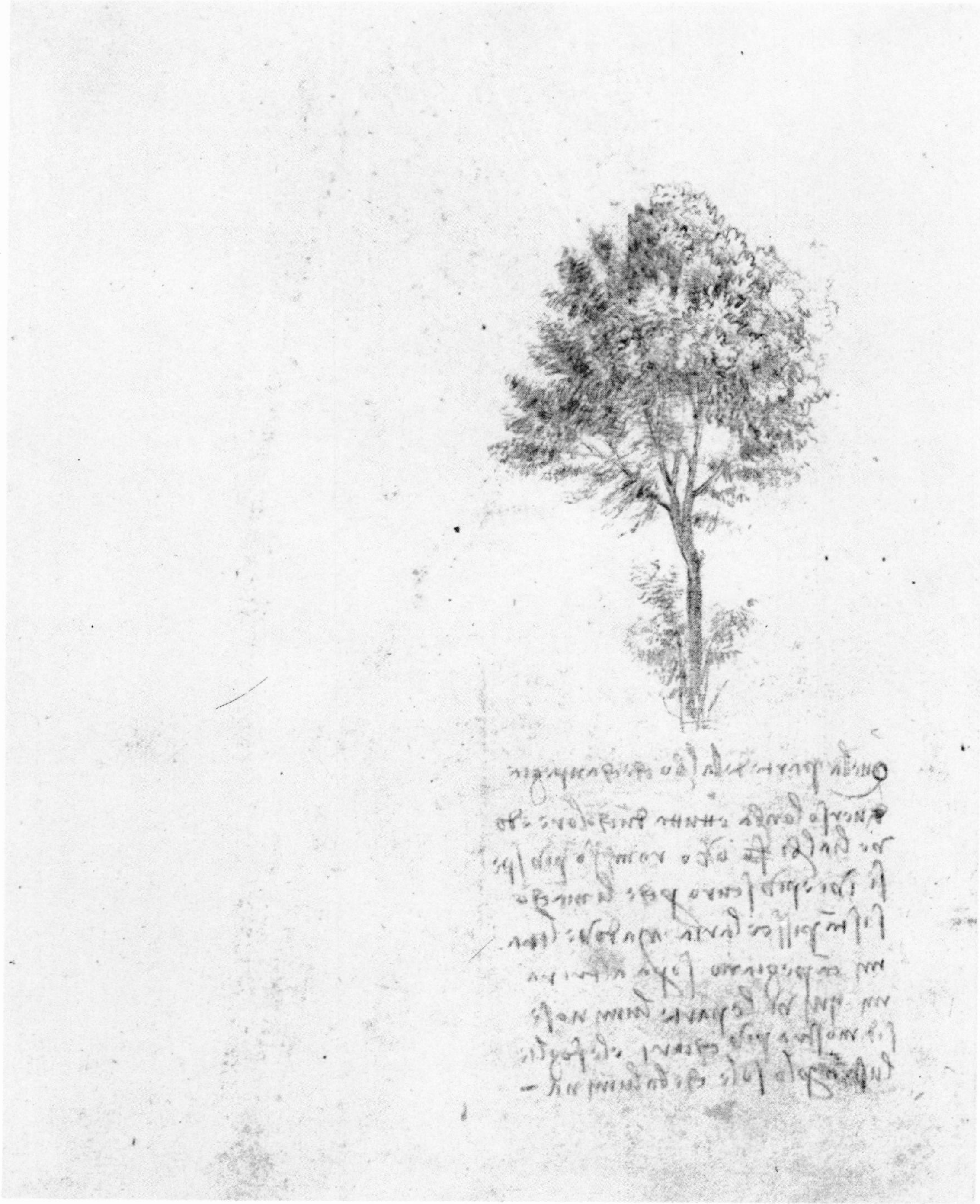

Study of a Tree, c. 1498. Red chalk. Below the drawing Leonardo wrote, "The part of a tree which has shadow for background is all of one tone, and wherever the trees or branches are thickest they will be darkest, because there are no little intervals of air. But where the boughs lie against a background of other boughs, the brighter parts are seen lightest and the leaves lustrous from the sunlight falling on them." Windsor; reproduced by gracious permission of Her Majesty the Queen

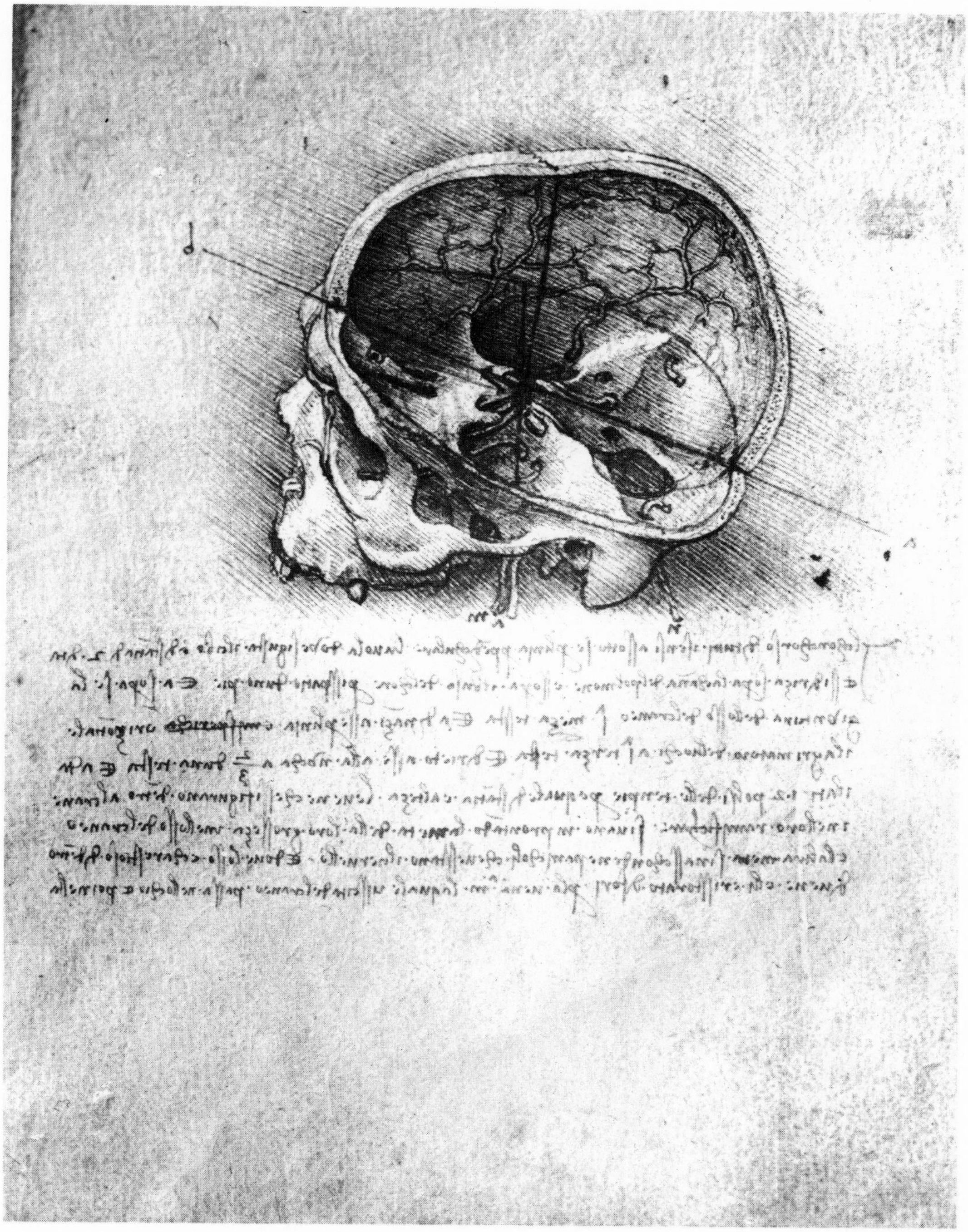

Anatomical Drawing of a Skull, 1489. Pen and ink. Where the lines intersect "there will be the meeting place of all the senses," Leonardo wrote. "The veins which are shown within the cranium in their ramification produce an imprint of half their thickness in the bone of the cranium, and the other half is hidden in the membranes which clothe the brain." Windsor; reproduced by gracious permission of Her Majesty the Queen

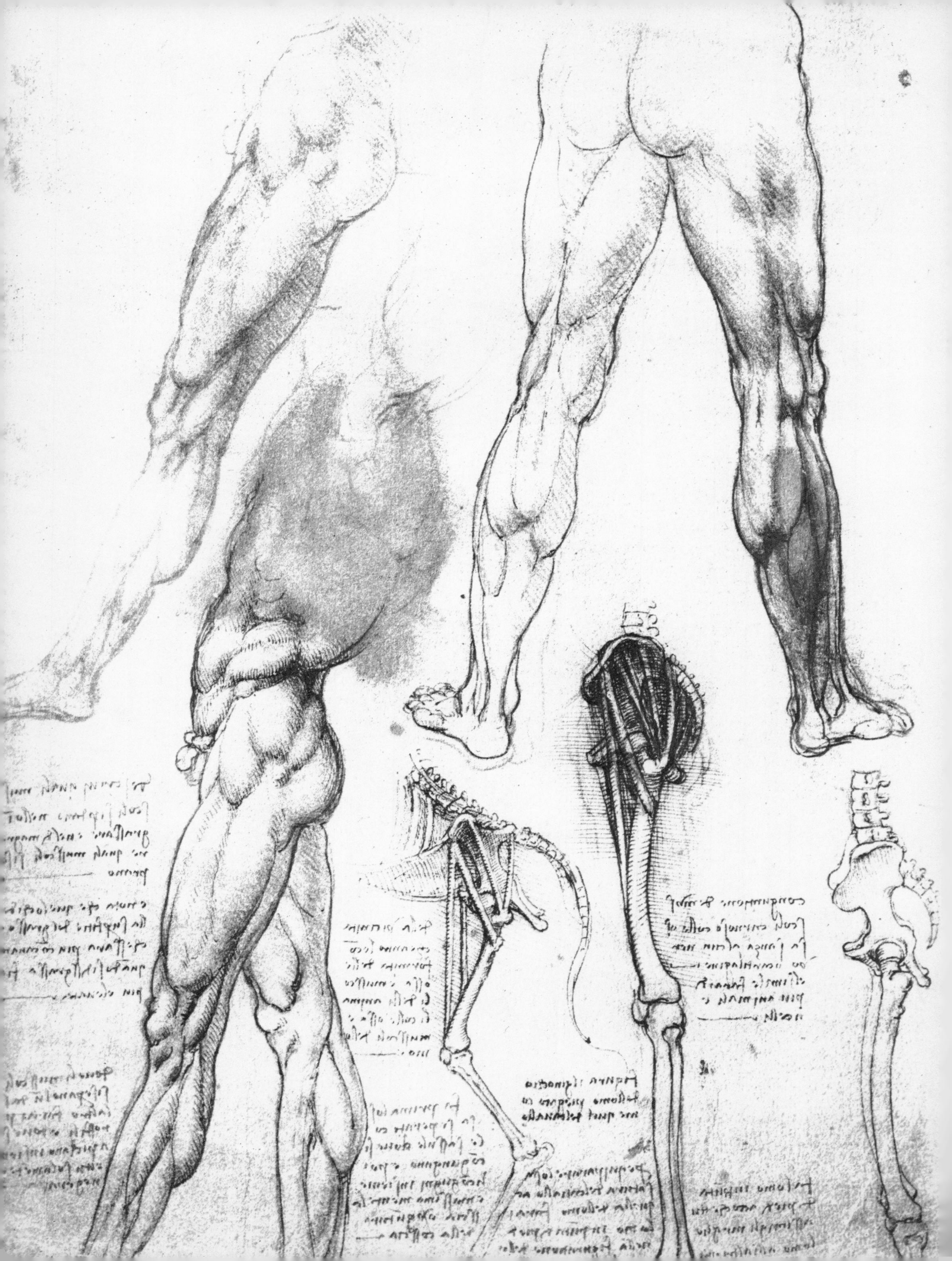

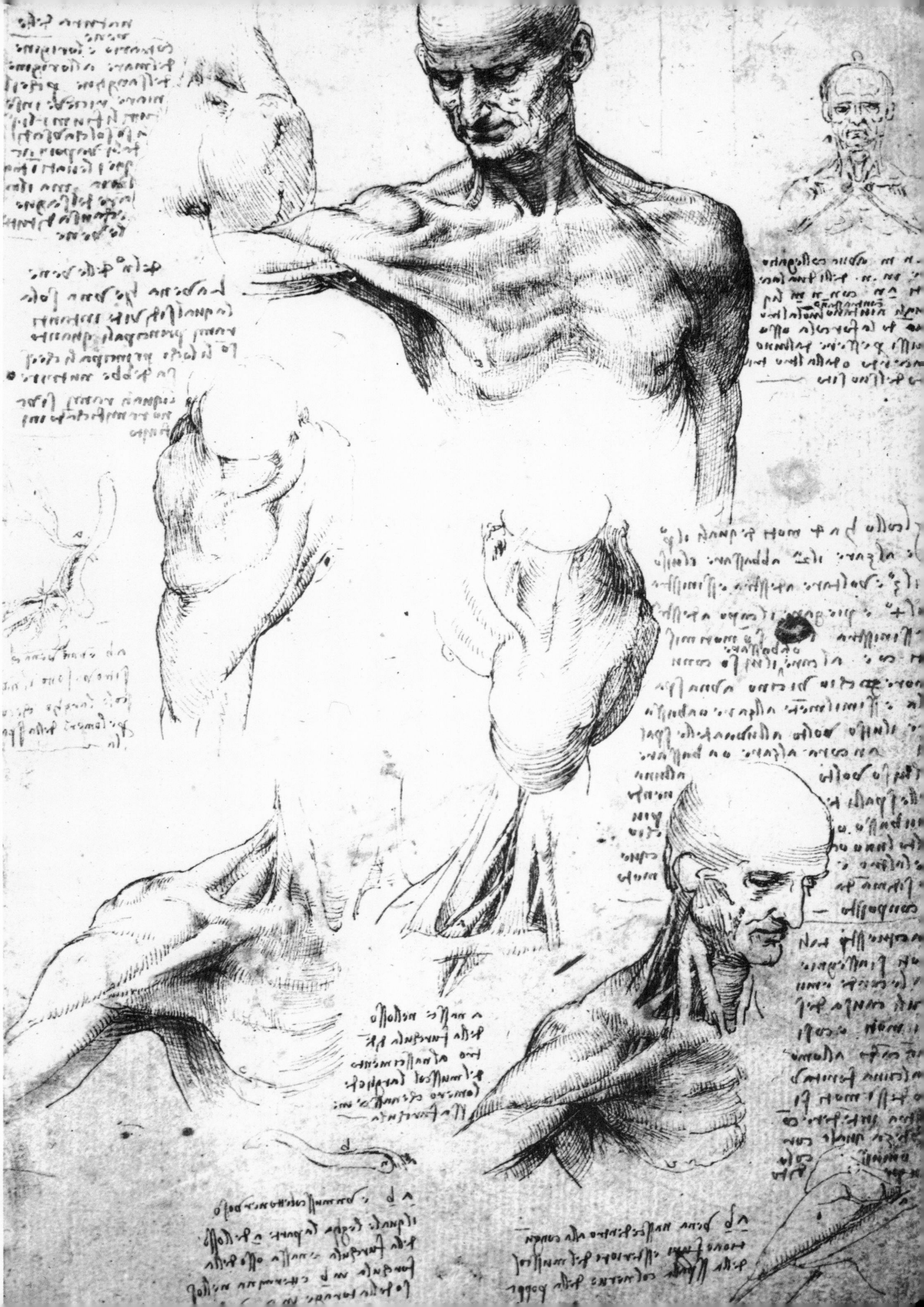

Page 82: Anatomical Study of a Man's Leg and a Dog's, c. 1504. Pen and ink over red chalk on red prepared paper. A drawing to show "the relationship that exists between the arrangement of the bones and muscles of animals and that of the bones and muscles of man." Windsor; reproduced by gracious permission of Her Majesty the Queen

Page 83: Anatomical Study of a Man's Shoulder, 1510. Pen and ink. An example of Leonardo's system of showing the part of anatomy being studied from different angles to make its structure and function clear. "Make a demonstration with muscles lean and thin," he wrote, "so that the space that is produced between the one and the other may make a window to show what is behind them." Windsor; reproduced by gracious permission of Her Majesty the Queen

Dissection of the Principal Organs of a Woman, c. 1510. Pen and ink and wash over black chalk, 18⅜″ × 12⅞″. In his notes on "the order of the book" of anatomy Leonardo wrote that "three dissections must be devoted to the female body. In this there is a great mystery, because of the womb and its embryo." Windsor; reproduced by gracious permission of Her Majesty the Queen

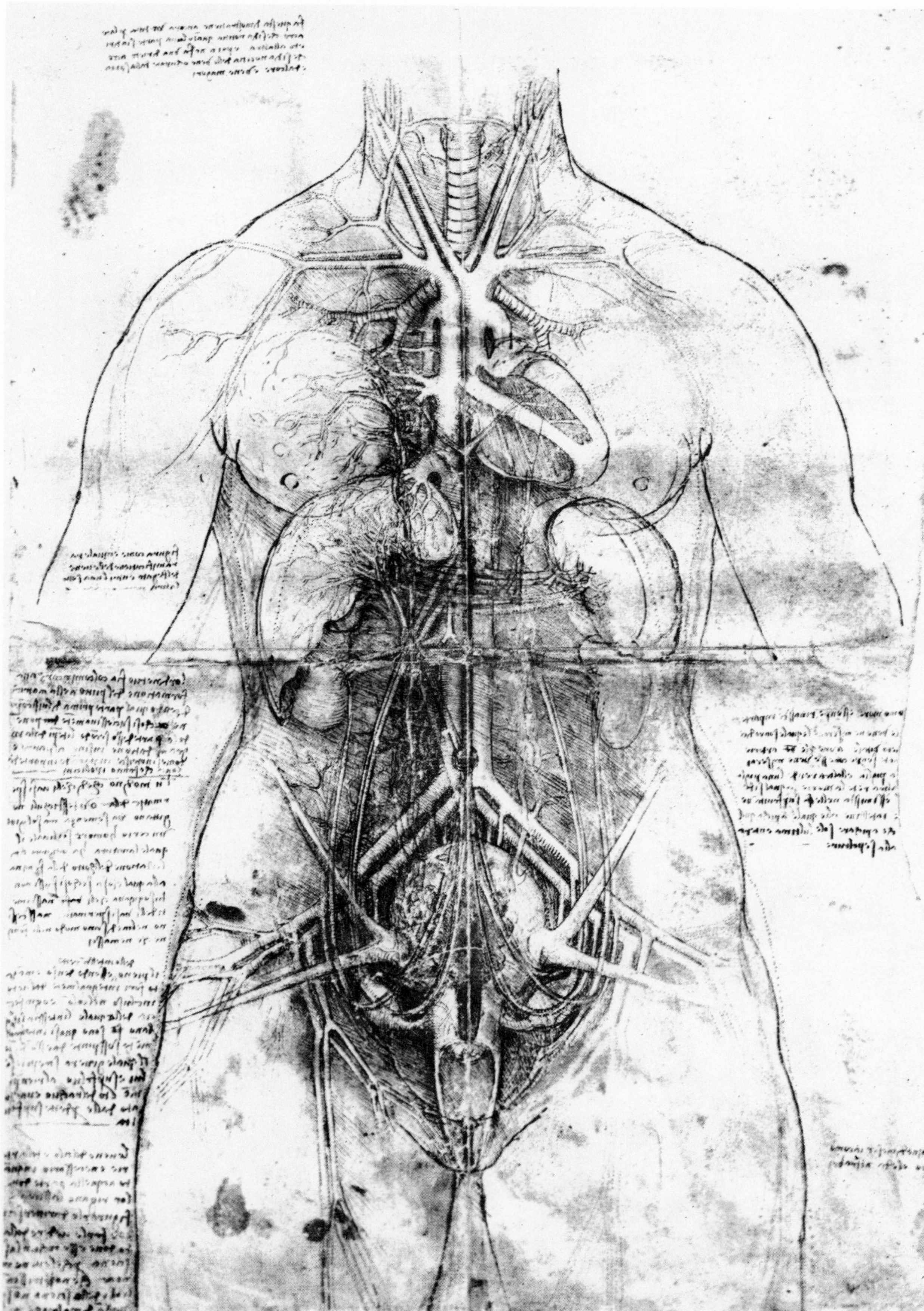

"The Vital Humor of This Arid Earth"

"It is the property of water," Leonardo wrote, "that it constitutes the vital humor of this arid earth." Still holding the medieval idea of the four humors, or fluids, which govern both health and disposition, he likened the flow of water in the earth, from the heights to the sea and then back again in a continuous process, to the flow of the blood through the body. Observing the distribution of silt in rivers, he deduced the process by which sedimentary rocks are formed, and recognized that the strata bearing fossils of shells and fish and other marine life, often found at great heights, were originally formed by the action of water, and that where there are now mountains there was once a sea or great lake. He noticed that on the surface of rock layers "there are still to be found the traces of the worms which crawled upon them when they were not yet dry, and all marine clays still contain shells, and the shells are petrified together with the clay."

He could not hold with the doctrine that, since in the process of creation, believed to have been about six thousand years earlier, land and sea were separated on the third day, and animal life created only on the fifth, the fossils and remains of marine life found in rocks were either the result of a mysterious action of the stars or left by the deluge which Noah rode out successfully in the ark. Instead, he regarded "the conches, oysters, and other similar animals that are born in the sea ooze" as "witnesses to us of the changing of the earth," and his imagination conjured up vast panoramas of prehistoric time. "Over the plains of Italy, where now birds fly in flocks," he wrote, "fish were wont to roam in large shoals." He perceived the constant process of slow geologic change going on everywhere, with water as the primary force. "Mountains," he observed, "are destroyed by rains and rivers." He studied water in all its forms, as snow and ice, as cloud and steam. He saw the resulting rain when clouds, "which are mists drawn up by the heat of the Sun," meet colder air; devised an instrument to measure humidity to know "when it is going to rain"; and recognized the rainbow as the effect of light on an atmosphere dense with moisture.

From a practical point of view he saw water as "the drayman of nature," and his notebooks are full of drawings of waterwheels of all sorts, including a cased wheel that is actually an early form of a turbine or hydraulic motor; and many of the various machines he devised were intended to be powered by water. The screw of Archimedes, a device of spiral, twisted pipes, which, through rotation, raises water from a lower to a higher level, also appears several times. It is the most famous of the many inventions of the Sicilian Greek of the third century who was the virtual founder of the science of mechanics.

Storm Breaking over an Alpine Valley, c. 1499. Red chalk. "The air moves like a river," Leonardo wrote, "and carries the clouds with it, just as running water carries all the things that float upon it." Windsor; reproduced by gracious permission of Her Majesty the Queen

Leonardo was fascinated with the movement of water as well as its use. He studied the rise and fall of the tides and the flow of springs, and many sketches show his unusual powers of observation in analyzing currents and other properties of water. "A wave," he noted, "is a reflected impression of percussion." He compared it to "the May wind . . . in the grain, and the wave is seen to travel over the field, and the stalks of grain do not move from their place." He made the experiment of dropping two small stones into still water and saw that "around the two percussions numerous separate circles are formed: these will meet as they increase in size and then penetrate and intersect one another all the while maintaining . . . their respective centers." He concluded that "the water, though apparently moving, does not . . . the reaction of the water being in the nature of a tremor rather than a movement . . . and as the water is of the same quality all through, its parts transmit the tremor to one another without change of position." He believed that the same thing

Old Man Meditating, and Studies of Swirling Water, c. 1510. Pen and ink. In the inscription Leonardo notes that "the motion of the surface of the water . . . resembles that of hair," and that "the water forms eddying whirlpools, partly due to the impetus of the principal current, and partly to the incidental motion and return flow." Windsor; reproduced by gracious permission of Her Majesty the Queen

happened to both sound and light, though noting the great difference in their rate of travel, thus instinctively anticipating the modern wave theory.

The close study of water and of the structure of the landscape was useful to him in the many canal projects in which he was engaged throughout the greater part of his life. The Romans had been great hydraulic engineers, as their aqueducts, a number of which are still in use in modern Rome, dramatically prove. During the later Middle Ages there was an attempt in the region of the Lombard Lakes to revive the ancient system of canals for transportation and for irrigation, adding considerably to agricultural productivity.

Canals were very important for the economy of the duchy of Milan, and Leonardo had the responsibility, as an engineer for Ludovico, of maintaining channels and locks as well as laying out additions to the system. His notebooks are full of drawings of details of locks, sluice gates, weirs, dikes, and pumps, most of which are of forms then in use. Aware as he was of the powerful erosive force of water, Leonardo was much interested in observing the course of rivers and in flood control. He conceived a grand plan for shifting the course of the Arno between Florence and the sea from its natural bed into a channel with controlled water level, useful for barge traffic and for irrigation as well as for supplying power to mills. From an engineering point of view, it was well conceived. The scheme called for transforming the valley of the River Chiana, a tributary of the Arno, south of Florence near Arezzo and Cortona, into a storage reservoir, to restore in part an ancient Roman system. War with Pisa narrowed the purpose of the project to a ship canal to give Florence access to the sea, but expense and politics brought the work to an end after only two years. Those who have seen the Arno in spring flood, its brown waters overflowing the lower parts of its valley and scouring away its banks, later to shrink to a rivulet, will recognize the purpose and the value of the scheme.

Other such projects were planned for Cesare Borgia north of Rome and in the district of the Romagna, that part of the Papal States east of Florence toward the Adriatic; and for Pope

Dredge, c. 1475–80. Pen and ink. "This is the way to dredge a harbor," Leonardo wrote as he explained the action of the plow on the bottom, and how it was to be dragged and then raised by windlasses when full. He intended that the rear end of the plow be "perforated . . . so that the water may not be shut within the box." Ambrosiana, Milan

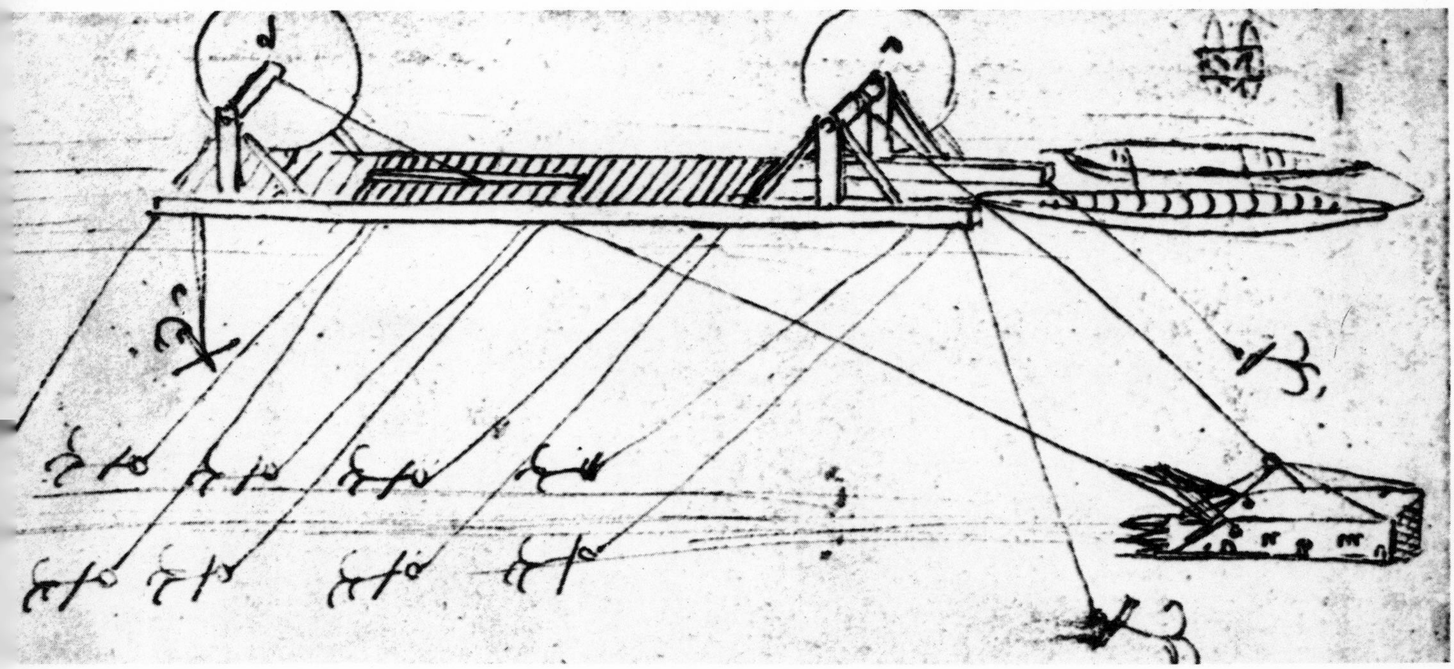

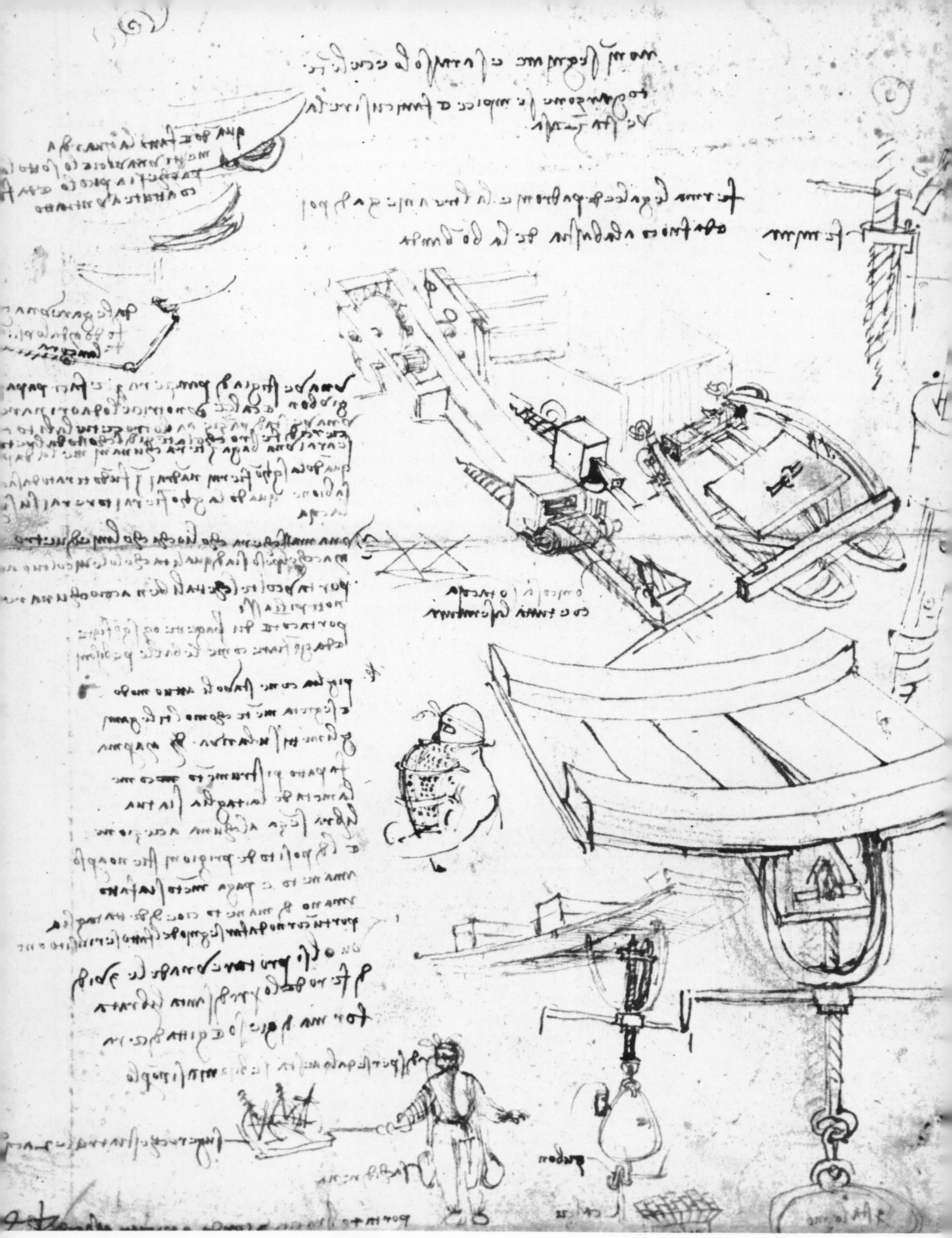

Leo X he devised a drainage system, realized only in our own century, for the Pontine Marshes. Later he laid out a canal system in the valley of the Loire for Francis I. It is said to have included a link between the Loire and the Seine, which became the central artery of France's great network of canals, completed many years after Leonardo's death. For the heavy work on such undertakings he perfected many machines and invented others, among them cranes, both double and single; lifting devices working by pulleys and screws; dredges for clearing channels and harbors; and bridges, one of which had a separate upper level for foot passage.

He designed an unsinkable ship and a life preserver, and had the notion of walking on the surface of the water by means of inflated shoes, much like floating snowshoes, assisted by two poles equipped at their lower ends with floats, though it is doubtful that he ever tried it out. He does seem to have tested devices for swimming under water, for which he also designed webbed gloves to add power to the stroke, and for diving. One of the latter involved a float containing the outlet and intake of a breathing apparatus with air hoses, that included an air storage tank to be strapped to the chest. Apparently he invented a still more effective way, but, he wrote, "I do not describe my method of remaining under water for as long a time as I can remain without food . . . on account of the evil nature of men, who would practice assassinations at the bottom of the sea by breaking the ships in their lowest parts and sinking them together with the crews who are in them." As we know, he devised several means for accomplishing just that purpose, and these, along with his diving apparatus, appeared in a number of later treatises on the art of war.

Studies of Diving Equipment and a Device for Underwater Attack on Ships, c. 1500. Pen and ink. The various sketches and notations seem to refer to the undersea attack Leonardo advised the Venetians to carry out against the Turkish Navy. Those referring to the diving apparatus are very detailed, including "a breastplate of armor together with hood, doublet, and hose, a small wineskin to urinate in, a dress for the armor, and a wineskin to contain the breath, with half a hoop of iron to keep it away from the chest . . . a mask with the eyes protruding made of glass," cork floats to keep the airlines straight, bags of sand for weights, and inflated wineskins for floats. Something of the commandolike attack he planned is suggested also: "When the watch has gone its round, bring a small skiff under the poop and set fire to the whole all of a sudden. . . . Carry a horn to give a signal whether the attempt has been successful or not. . . . Carry a knife that cuts well so that a net does not hold you prisoner." The device to sink galleys by springing their planking was designed to work on the principle of a familiar type of modern corkscrew. Ambrosiana, Milan

Outcrop of Stratified Rock, c. 1510–13. Pen and ink over black chalk. "The mighty rivers," Leonardo wrote, "always flow turbid because of the earth stirred up in them through the friction of their waters," which continuously carry it down to the ocean and uncover the layers of rock made up of mud and shells once deep beneath "the sea where they were born when the salt waters covered them. . . . And so the light surface of the earth is continually raised, and the . . . ancient beds of the sea become chains of mountains." Windsor; reproduced by gracious permission of Her Majesty the Queen

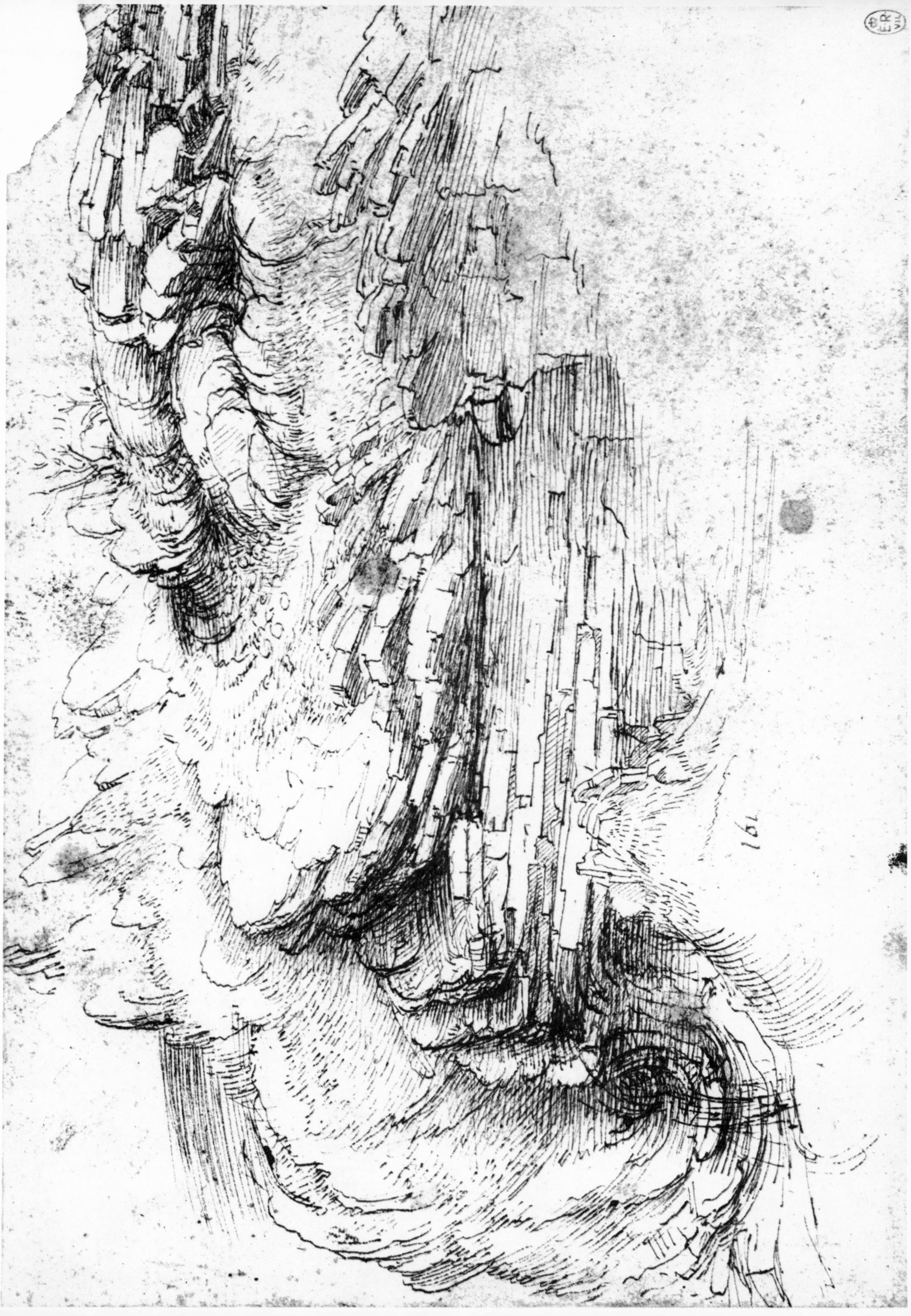

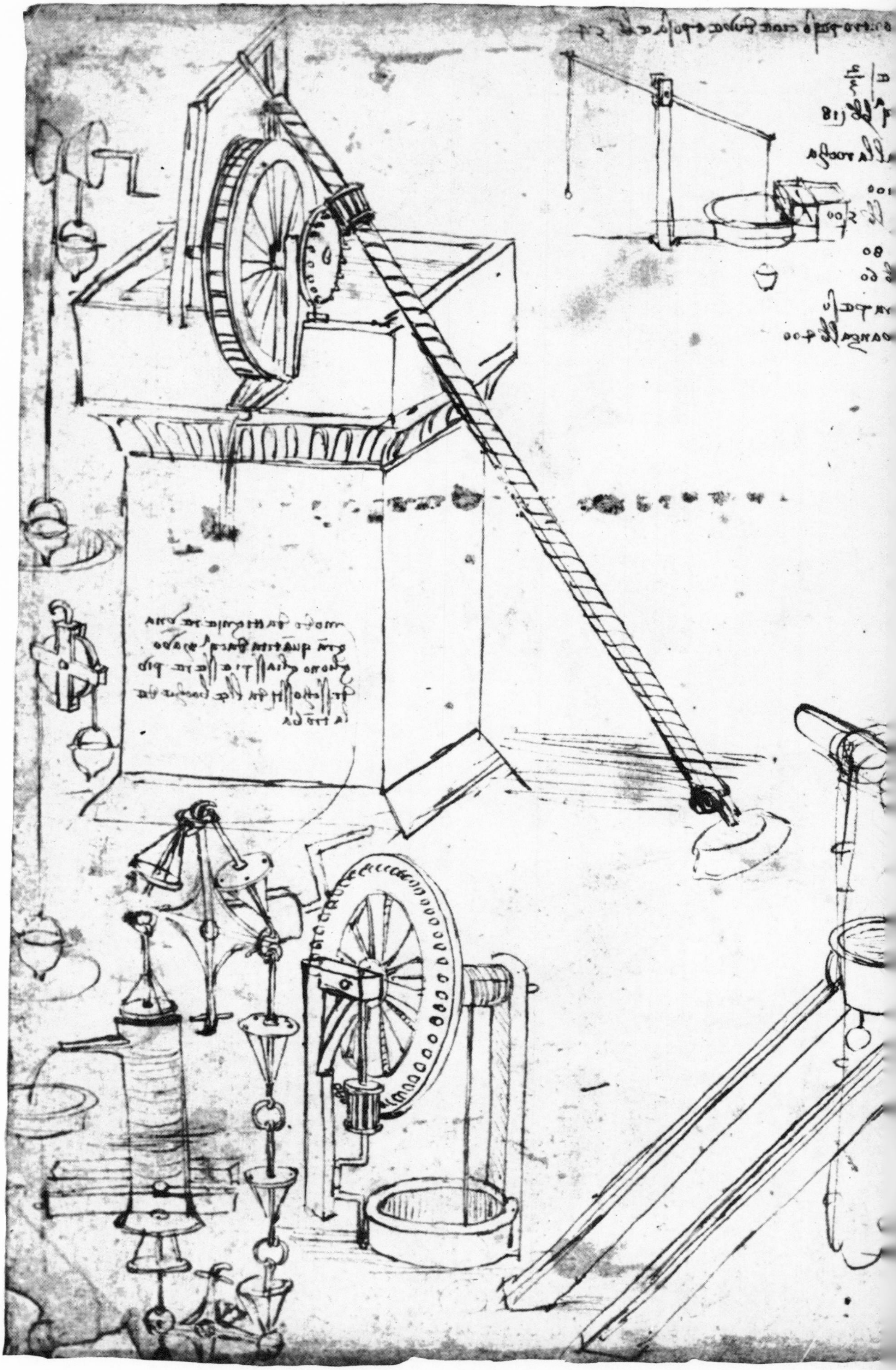

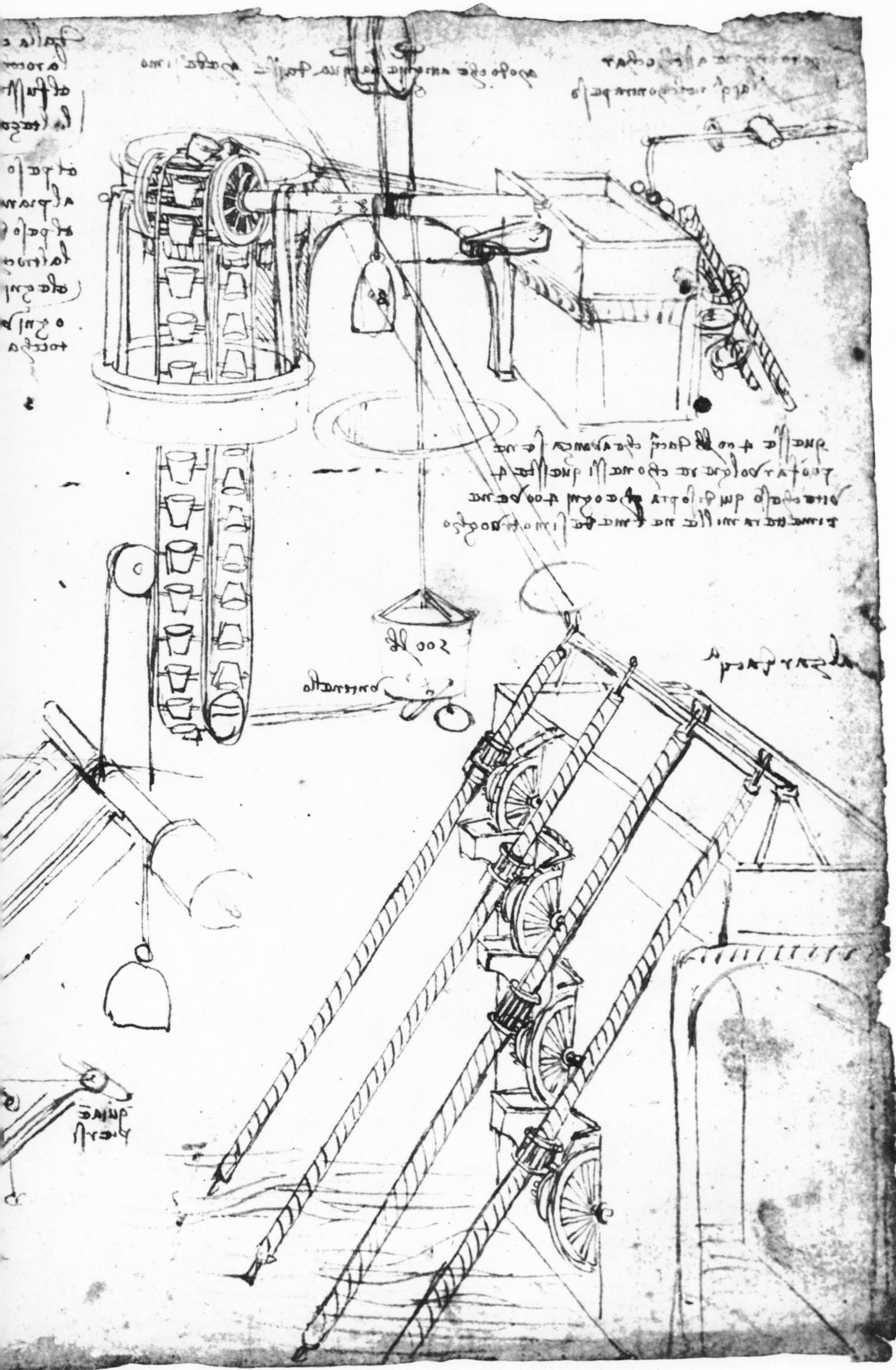

Pages 94–95: Various Devices for Raising Water, c. 1475–80. Pen and ink. Examples of Archimedes' screw, the invention of the third-century Greek engineer of that name, appear at upper left and lower right. His works were known during the Middle Ages, and Leonardo refers to them often. Ambrosiana, Milan

Canal with Two Locks, c. 1475–80. Pen and ink. The weirs, or low dams, which Leonardo called "steps," were to control the drop in water level. The working of the lock is detailed at the left. Ambrosiana, Milan

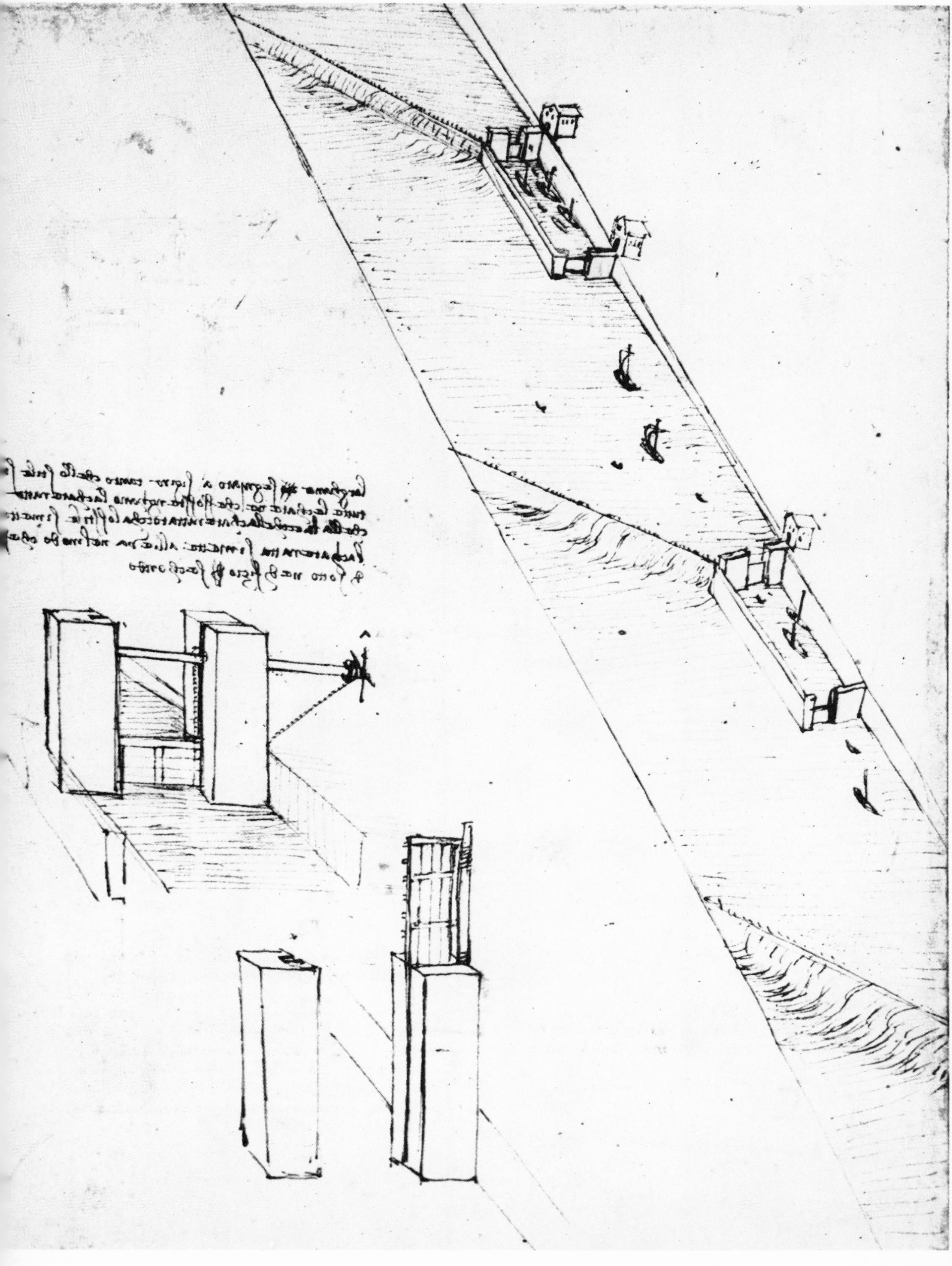

A Lock Gate for a Canal, c. 1475–80. Pen and ink. The small door detailed below was to allow the lock to fill smoothly, an invention of Leonardo's that was in general use in the canals of France fifty years later. The meeting edges of the gates are beveled so that they close at a broad angle, thus being forced more tightly shut by the pressure of water from upstream. The bottom of the lock is paved to prevent scouring by the rush of water when the lock is used. Ambrosiana, Milan

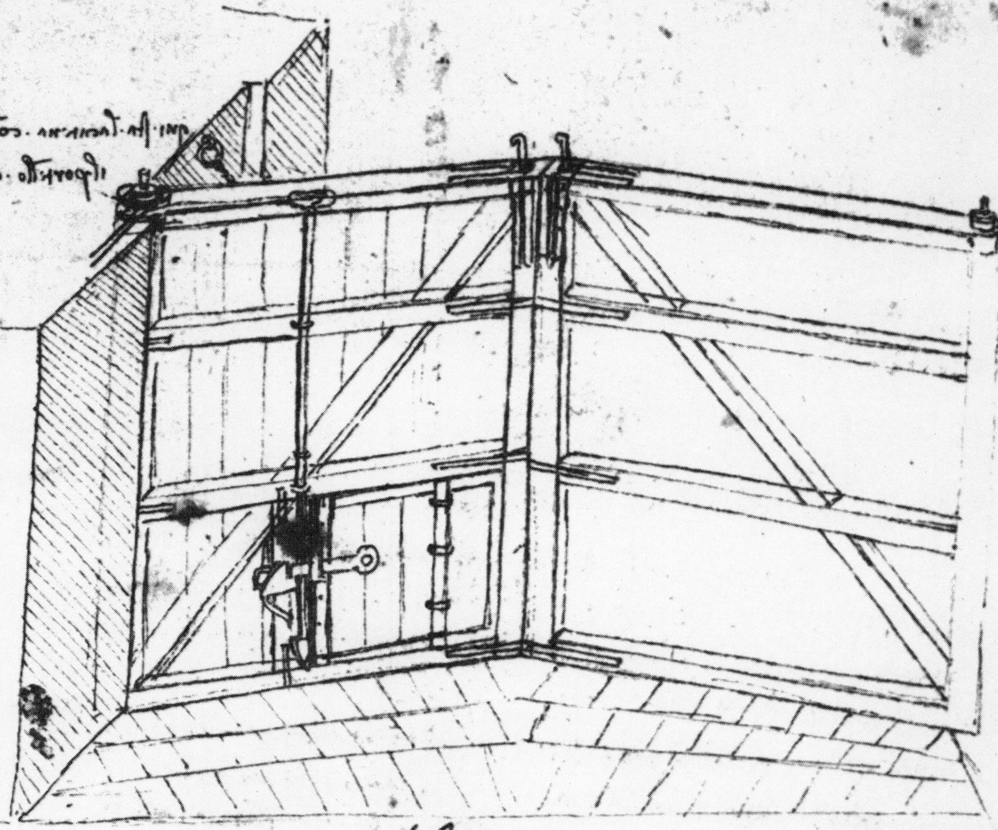

10

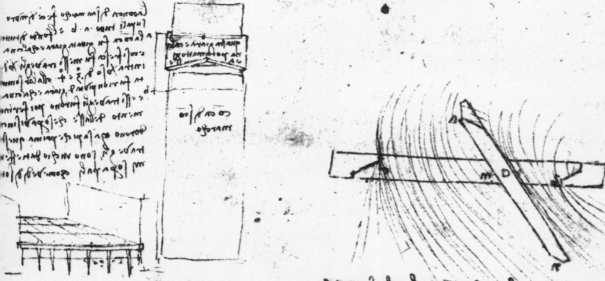

Double Crane, c. 1475–80. Pen and ink and wash. A machine designed by Leonardo for canal digging. Ambrosiana, Milan

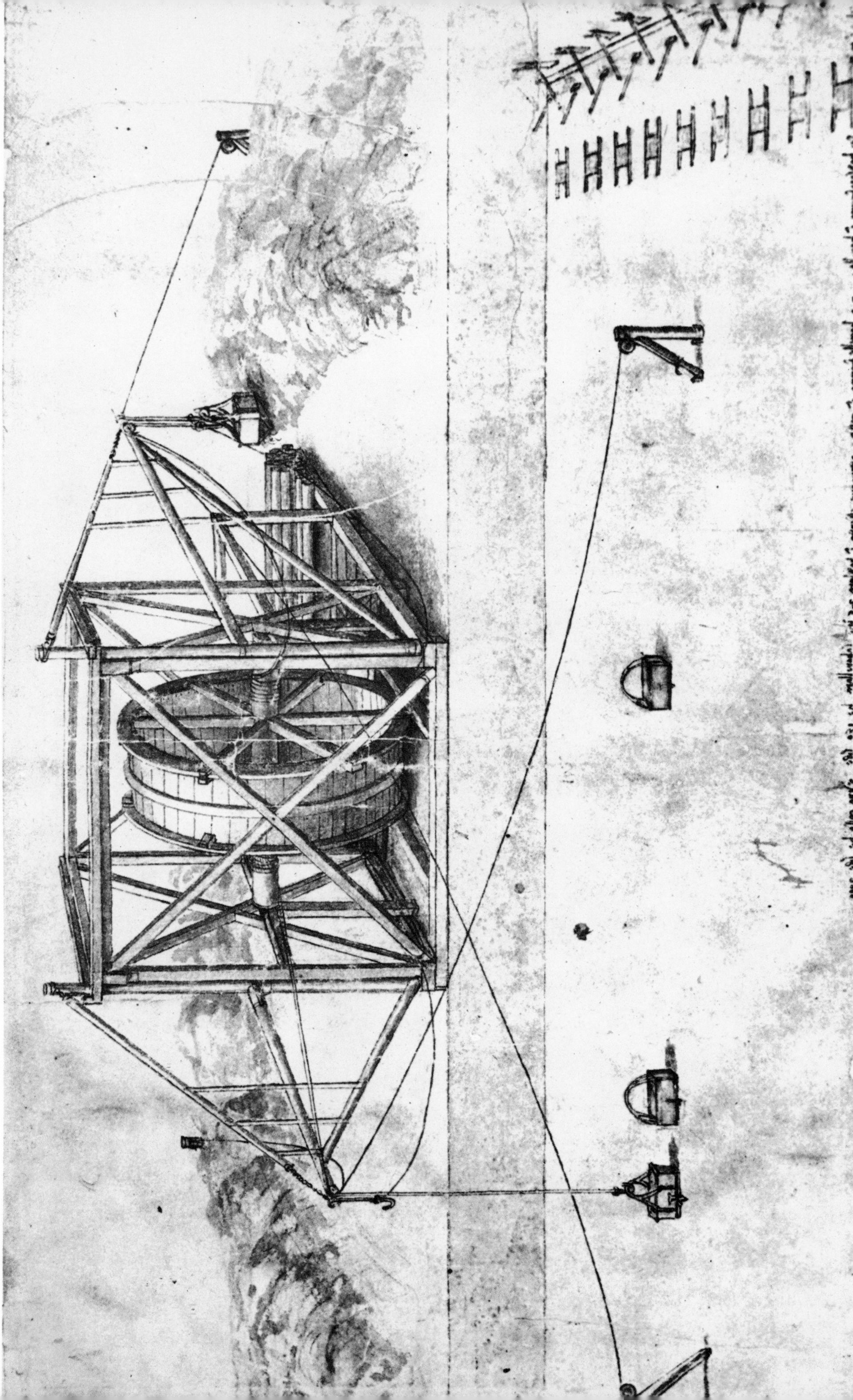

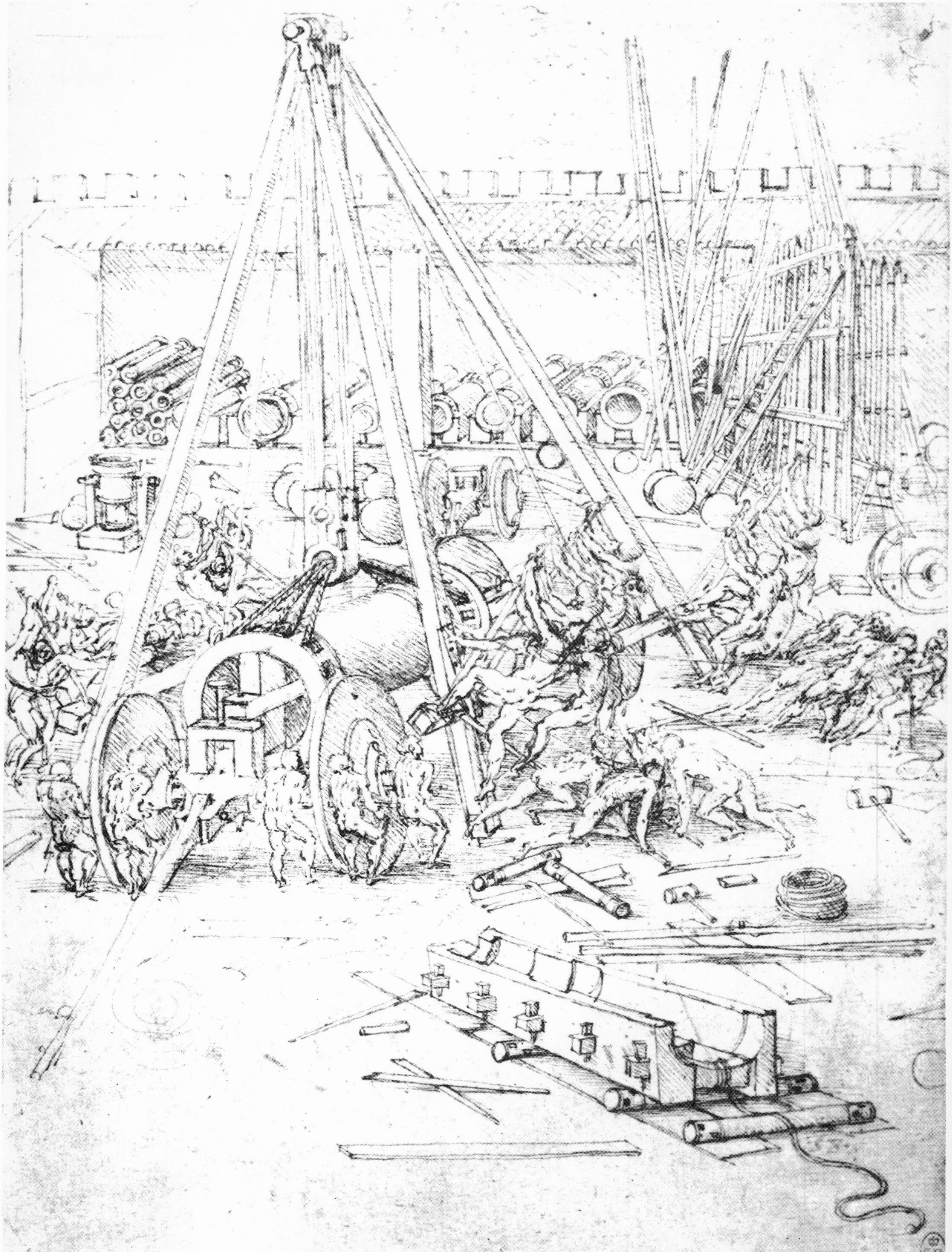

"Many Most Powerful Machines of War"

Though Leonardo considered war "a most bestial madness," it is a revealing commentary on the history of man that, as George Sarton, the distinguished historian of science, has pointed out,

> the only branch of technology that has never become inactive is the art of warfare. . . . Most technicians were concerned with that art, trying to find new weapons, to improve the old ones, or to defend themselves more effectively against the weapons of their enemies. The invention of new arms and new armor was always the obsession of men, good or bad. Even as great an artist and as serene a man as Leonardo da Vinci was obliged to devote much of his attention to such problems.

War was a fact of life during his period as during so many others in the troubled history of man. There seemed no escape from it, so, as a realist, Leonardo accepted it as inevitable though deplorable. "How criminal it is," he believed, "to take the life of a man." Though violence and war were everywhere around him, he was quite clear as to his primary purpose as a military engineer. "When besieged by ambitious tyrants," he wrote in his notes on warfare, "I find a means of offense and defense in order to preserve the chief gift of nature, which is liberty."

The Renaissance inherited from the Middle Ages a considerable arsenal of weapons as well as a body of accepted theory of offensive and defensive tactics. The artillery of ancient times had been based on the ballistic principle, the use of the recoil resulting from twisting cables, made of braided or intertwined sinews, wound around a windlass and suddenly released by a trigger, thus shooting stones and fireballs, or occasionally, as a subtle gesture of disrespect for the enemy, a dead animal or a captured comrade. Early in the Middle Ages *trébushets,* as the French called them, or in Italian, *trabocchi,* were developed, first recorded as used by the Normans during the siege of Paris in 886. They were gigantic slings for throwing objects and worked on the principle of the lever in the form of a counterweighted arm. The arm, a heavy beam weighted at the lower end, was hauled downward by a windlass and then released suddenly so that it was jerked upright by the weight, the missile attaining yet greater velocity by being in a sling attached to the violently swinging upper end. The mangonel was a similar device for projecting stones or javelins, and was used by the Moslems as early as 806 to hurl fireballs. Such engines were often colossal in size, needing the strength of a crew of men to work the winches.

In the twelfth century a new and more deadly weapon was added to the medieval arsenal—the crossbow—made not of wood but of metal. It had so much spring that, in later models, the bowman had to use a lever or a small windlass to pull back the wire that had replaced the earlier string. Its bolt, or short arrow, traveled

---

Courtyard of a Foundry, c. 1487. Pen and ink on brownish paper. Windsor; reproduced by gracious permission of Her Majesty the Queen

with great speed and had considerable power of penetration, especially at shorter distances. It appeared so formidable a destructive device that its use against Christians was unsuccessfully outlawed by the Lateran Council of 1139. The long bow, which showed its effectiveness in the English victories in France, at Crécy in 1346 and Agincourt in 1415, was at its best a longer-range weapon. Its proper use required a great deal of training and skill, and consequently it did not play as significant a part in warfare on the Continent as might be expected.

Another deadly invention was that of Greek Fire, so called because of its development and use by the Byzantine Greeks of the Eastern Roman Empire whose capital was Constantinople. Made of a mixture of naphtha, quick lime, and crude oil, it was used in maritime warfare. It burst into intense flame when it touched water, while the oil made it both spread and cling, "so eager to burn that it will run along wood even when it is under water," Leonardo noted. It proved so decisive that, as a closely guarded secret of the Byzantine state, it was credited with halting the expansion of the Saracen armies, until then almost invincible, late in the seventh century.

The introduction of gunpowder was the most revolutionary innovation of its kind during the era. The Chinese had it by the tenth century, and its use was known in Europe before 1300. Firearms appeared almost immediately and by 1350 had become common. The earliest cannon were clumsy pieces made of iron bars soldered together and strengthened with iron bands rather like barrel hoops. Gunpowder was used not only for firing projectiles from cannon, mortars, and smaller arms, but also for increasing the destructiveness of grenades. Previously they had been loaded with a mixture of saltpeter, sulphur, and coal dust that must have been almost as explosive as the early forms of gunpower, made of saltpeter, sulphur, and charcoal. The use of Greek Fire was made more devastating by mixing it with gunpowder so that it was not only more explosive, but also would work on land as well as water.

Siege towers, battering rams, and mining operations, either to get troops into an enemy stronghold or to undermine and cause the collapse of walls, were all employed much as in the days of the Roman Empire. Methods were used to build temporary bridges similar to that mentioned in Book IV of Caesar's *Gallic Wars,* with its system of pilings whose rigidity "naturally increased in proportion to the current's force," the technical description of which used to afford endless difficulties in translation to generations of students of Latin.

Vitruvius, the Roman architect and engineer who is thought to have seen military service with Julius Caesar, wrote at length on the construction and use of catapults or scorpions, versions of the *ballista* that often shot heavy, spearlike arrows. He described the tortoise, a movable shed mounted on wheels and used to protect workmen while they filled a moat in order to get close enough to a wall to use a battering ram or siege tower. He cited, as an example of the latter, one designed by Hegetor of Byzantium that was sixty-three feet long by forty-two wide and thirty-six high, roofed in heavy timber covered with rawhide to withstand fire, and with an iron-beaked ram 180 feet long. This immense contraption had wheels six and a half feet high and three feet thick, and could move forward, backward, and sideways by means of levers, stuck into holes in the movable axles, and a limitless amount of manpower. It is doubtful that there were many monsters like this, but such oversize equipment may have suggested to Leonardo some of his colossal military machines.

Defensive architecture, which was to be so radically changed in later centuries when the fuller potential of gunpowder and the development of more effective artillery were realized, was still deeply indebted during the Renaissance to Roman precedent. The system of crenellated walls with corner towers and reinforced gateways, projecting for raking fire at an enemy trying to force or scale the walls, the use of moats and drawbridges, and of inner and outer fortifications were all a part of Roman practice. There were some refinements that resulted from the experience of the Crusades, when military engineers of western Europe saw the methods of the Byzantines and the Saracens very much at first hand, but there was little essential difference from previous construction.

A considerable amount of military lore had come down to the men of the Renaissance and the recent discovery of additional works, such as that of Vitruvius, added still more. By Leonardo's period there were professional military engineers of real competence. Among them were such distinguished individuals as Francesco di Giorgio of Siena, who was also an architect, sculptor, and painter; and Roberto Valturio, whose military treatise, published in Latin in 1472 and in Italian in 1483 in Verona, Leonardo owned and used. For centuries the military engineer had not only been respected for his special knowledge, often handed down in secret from father to son, but had also had much to do with civil engineering and architecture. Furthermore, as practical men and doers, they were for the most part the only practicing scientists, since the university men and scholars limited themselves almost entirely to the realm of theory based on accepted ancient authority. Therefore the treatises of the military engineers often deal with far more than engines of destruction and defense.

In offensive weapons Leonardo strove for increased firepower and speed, and deliberately set about devising machines to strike terror in the enemy. There was a chariot with wheels geared to whirling scythes to mow men down like grain, and others with wheels similarly geared to four whirling arms, to the ends of which were attached spiked war clubs or flails which were meant to swing with diabolical force and swiftness. On the same sheet with the scythed chariot appears his version of the tank, the "armored vehicle" mentioned in his letter to Ludovico. Its four wheels were to be propelled from inside by men turning cranks, while others fired small cannon at the enemy through slots provided for the purpose. It has wagonlike wheels rather than the treads of a modern tank, though it was clearly conceived to accomplish a similar purpose.

He designed a device to shoot arrows by

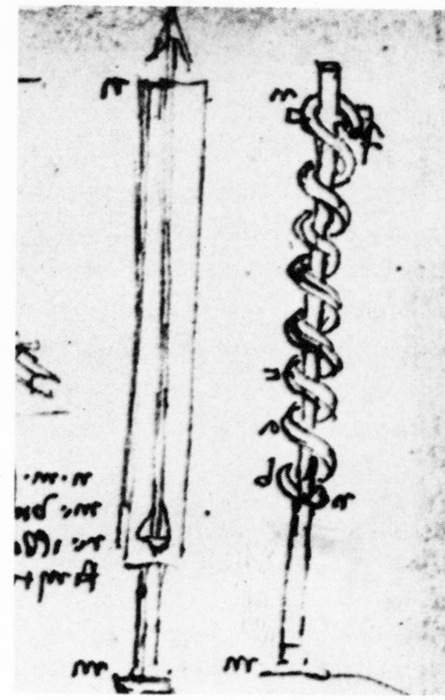

means of a coiled spring, and a number of crossbows, all large enough to be considered *ballistae,* but one of them so tremendous that it was surely beyond the capacity of engineers of the times to construct it. The length must have been planned to be about forty feet, with a bow of about thirty-six. Mounted on three pairs of wheels, canted inward at the top for added stability, it was to be set by a windlass turning a worm gear with a long screw. Its bolt would have been enormous and its force incalculable, as in the drawing a normal man looks like a Lilliputian beside it. Some of the other drawings of crossbows seem perfectly capable of realization, though the idea of mounting a number of them on a large vertical wheel in such a way that an almost continuous fire could be maintained as the wheel turned seems to be another fantastic device.

Leonardo designed mangonels with multiple arms to quadruple their firepower, and catapults of all kinds, probably intended for hurling fireballs loaded with shrapnel meant to explode on contact. One of these he describes as two and a half *braccia* (nearly five feet) in diameter, "made of melted pitch, sulphur, and tow of hemp rubbed together" and heavily charged with both Greek Fire and explosive, as well as fragments of appropriately destructive material, to fill the air with fire and a cloud of exploding, flaming missiles when it struck.

The early cannon were generally not very large, and were made up of bars of iron, brass,

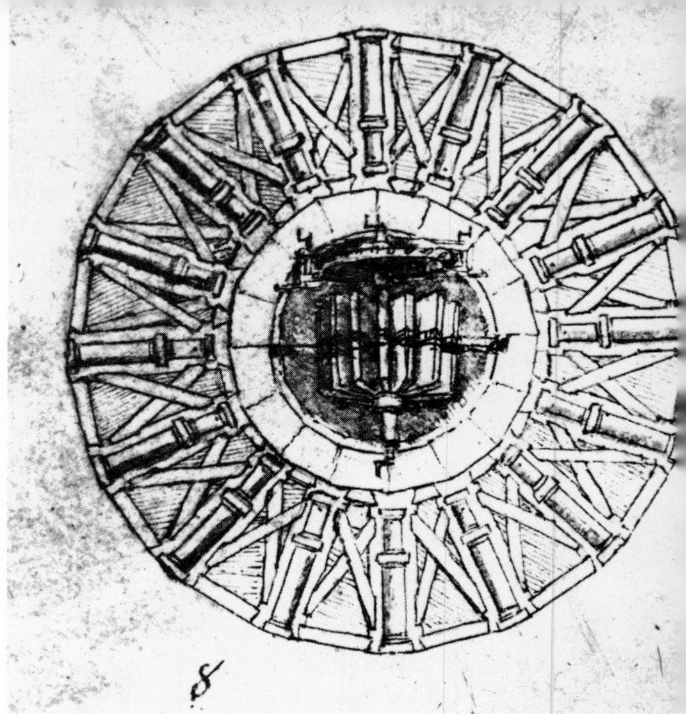

or bronze. But by Leonardo's day they had grown from about 150 pounds to upwards of six to eight hundred, though they continued largely to be made in the same awkward fashion. He had had early training in metallurgy in Verrocchio's shop and soon turned to solid castings that were then bored, in place of the older method.

That part of the bronze is most compressed within its mold which is most liquid. And that is most liquid which is hottest, and that is hottest which comes first out of the furnace. One ought, therefore, always to make first in the casting that part of the cannon which has to receive the powder before that which has to contain the muzzle.

He clearly favored breech loading instead of the then usual muzzle loading, and drew many mechanisms for this purpose. But the most interesting of his designs are those of multiple-firing cannon and a steam cannon. There are several drawings of the former, one with three sets of twelve barrels, each of which revolves so that while one set fires another cools and the third is reloaded. He had the idea of mounting sixteen cannon on a turntable to be rotated horizontally to maintain constant fire, while in another design the barrels radiate like a section of a fan so that, in firing, a small barrage could be laid down. The *architronito,* or steam cannon, is most ingenious, and seems to be unique, since the idea of using the power of steam at this period was virtually unknown. Based on the sudden expansive force of water turned to steam, the piece had the breech built into a basketlike brazier full of burning coals. When the shot was in place and the breech hot enough, the water, poured into "the heated part of the machine," was changed instantly into steam, the expansion involved propelling the ball.

Leonardo's designs for ordinary cannon have that handsome decorative quality which, until the nineteenth century, characterized all such military objects. Many of them appear to be large and heavy, suitable only for stationary use, while others are lighter, equipped with more maneuverable carriages, with ingenious elevating and aiming mechanisms, and are clearly intended for the field. He also designed bombards, or mortars, an early form of cannon with a short barrel and large bore, used to lob all sorts of missiles at an enemy. Leonardo, however, planned to use them with exploding projectiles to blanket an area with shrapnel. Some of the drawings illustrate his theory of saturating an entire strip of territory in front of a bastion or curtain wall as a lethally effective defensive

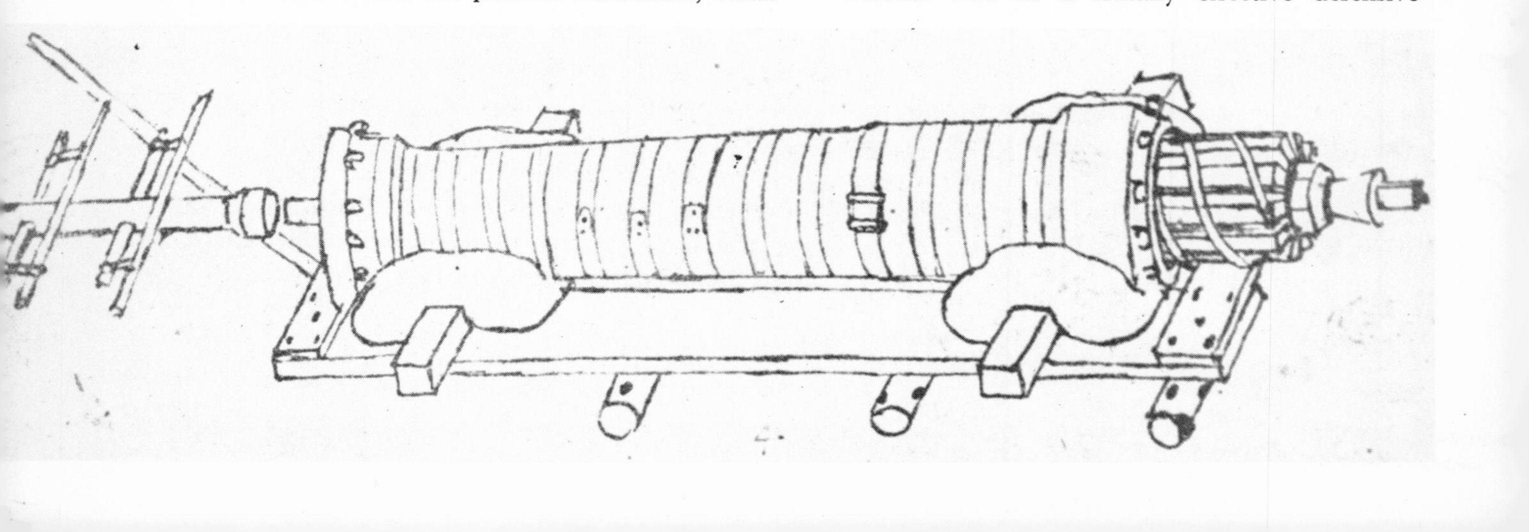

Cannon Construction, c. 1485–88. Pen and ink. The barrel is formed of iron staves welded together and bound with iron hoops. After the core is removed, the cannon is finished and polished. Ambrosiana, Milan

measure. Other projectiles are designed with aerodynamically sound directional fins in the manner of modern bombs and rockets, but whether they were to be hurled by catapults or fired from cannon remains unclear.

The notebooks contain an ingenious design for a scaling ladder, rather on the principle of that used for today's hook-and-ladder, and other devices to knock down an enemy's ladders while showering him with short-range missiles. Leonardo's movable towers, like various types of armament, and almost all his catapults and mangonels, are derived from Roberto Valturio's treatise *On Things Military,* and have extendible bridges for assaulting fortifications. There are designs for a variety of light and flexible assault ladders, and pitons, used for scaling the walls of a fortress, like those employed by modern mountaineers.

He drew several types of temporary bridges, made up of light, prefabricated units for easy portability, like those mentioned in his letter to Duke Ludovico. A swinging bridge for permanent installation, with a use very like that of a drawbridge, has a handsome and unusual arched truss that appears to anticipate the construction of the nineteenth century and later.

Among many other things calculated to cause "grave detriment and confusion" to an enemy is Leonardo's idea of laying down a poisonous smoke screen by "throwing among the enemy ships with small catapults, chalk, pulverized arsenic, and verdigris," pointing out that "all who inhale this powder will be asphyxiated by breathing it, but be careful that the wind be such as not to blow back the fumes." He then designed a kind of elementary gas mask for protection against such an attack, which seems not to have been attempted on a significant scale until the First World War.

Leonardo's studies of fortifications show his awareness of the changes necessary with the advent of artillery, and he figured the angles for the surfaces of the escarpment at the foot of walls, of salients, and of the sides of embrasures for deflecting enemy fire with as little damage as possible. Where medieval fortresses had high and relatively thin walls, with a generally unorganized system of towers, Leonardo reduced the height of the walls, thickened them, strengthened them with projecting towers for flanking fire, and protected them by moats, as in earlier structures. He eliminated the crenellated battlements, with their machicolations through which the defenders poured boiling oil, hot pitch, or even more unpleasant substances onto the heads of the attackers below; with the great increase in firepower such things were no longer practical. His triangular bastions, projecting outward from the curtain wall, were of the form more completely developed by Marshal de Vauban, the great French military engineer of the late seventeenth century, while other fortifications he designed look forward to the eighteenth. And in the extraordinary circular fort with concentric ramparts that appears among the drawings, with its low, curved casemating for the deflection of fire, he anticipates such developments of earlier decades of our own century as the once famous but now forgotten Maginot Line.

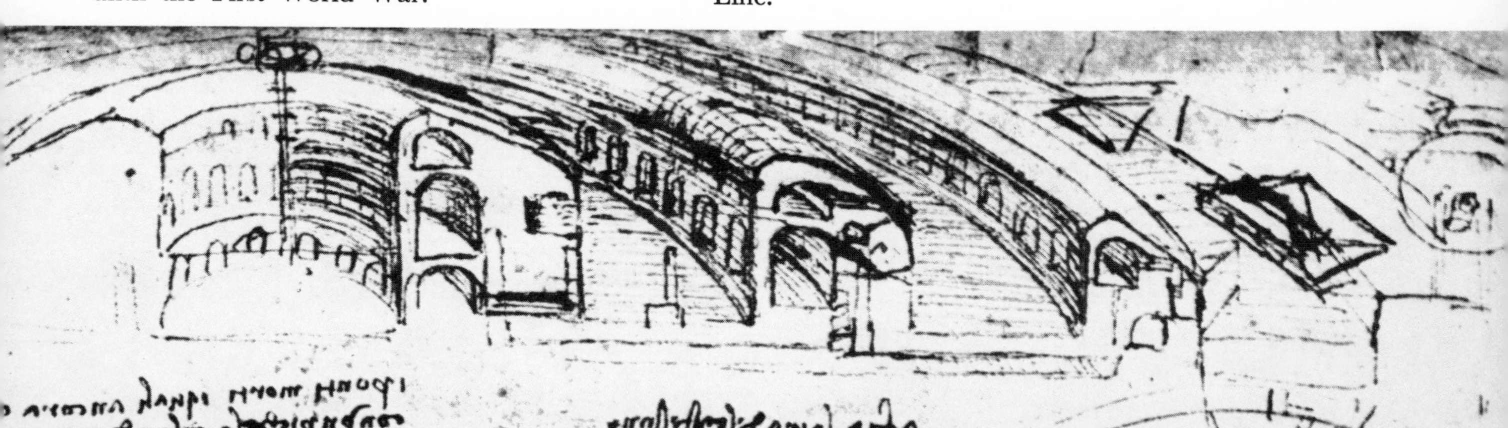

A Chariot Armed with Scythes, and a Tank, c. 1485–88. Pen and ink and wash. In his letter to Ludovico il Moro, Leonardo described such "armored vehicles, safe and unattackable, which entering among the enemy with their cannon, there is no body of men so great but they will break them. And behind them the infantry can follow quite without hindrance." British Museum, London

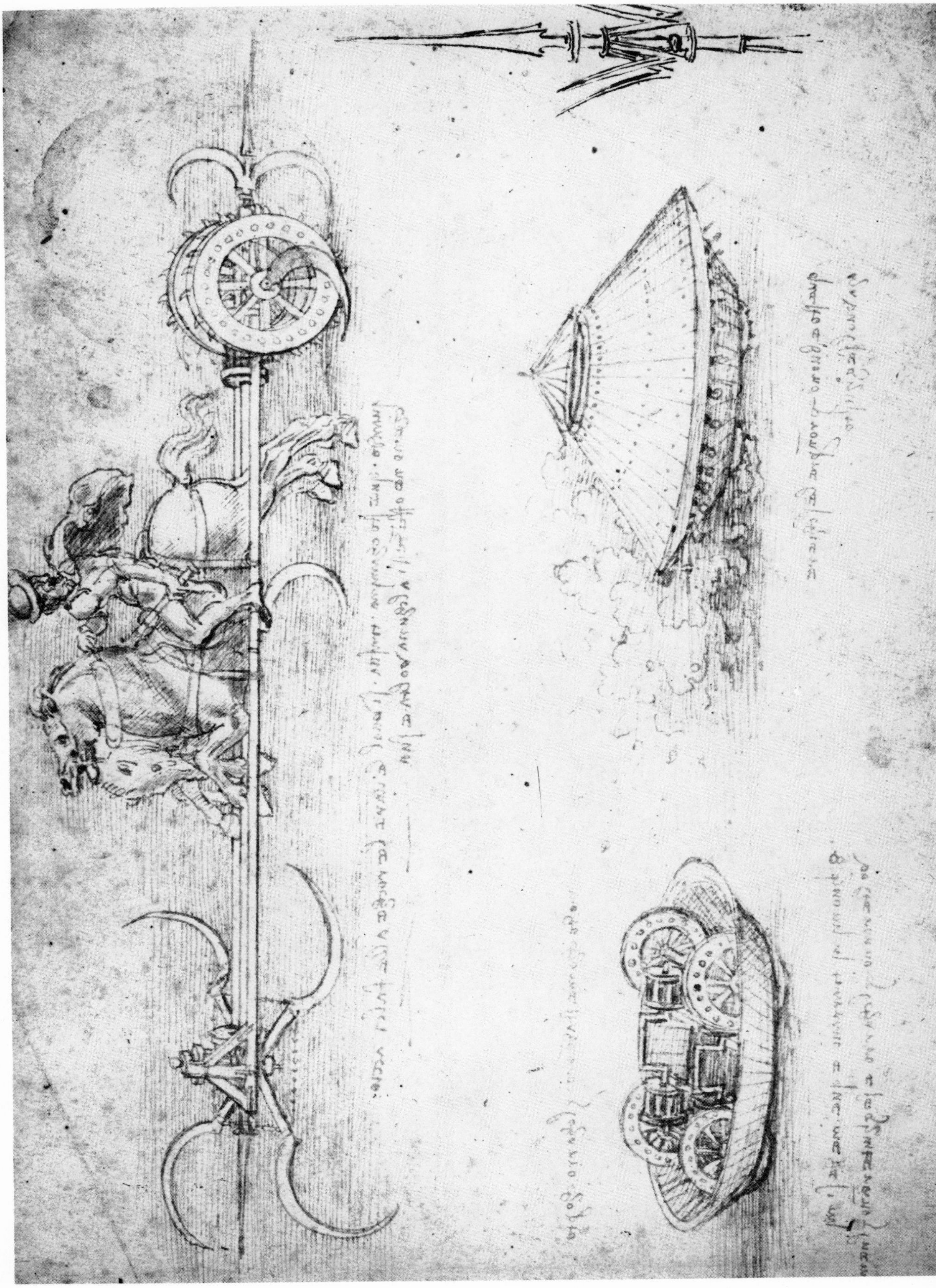

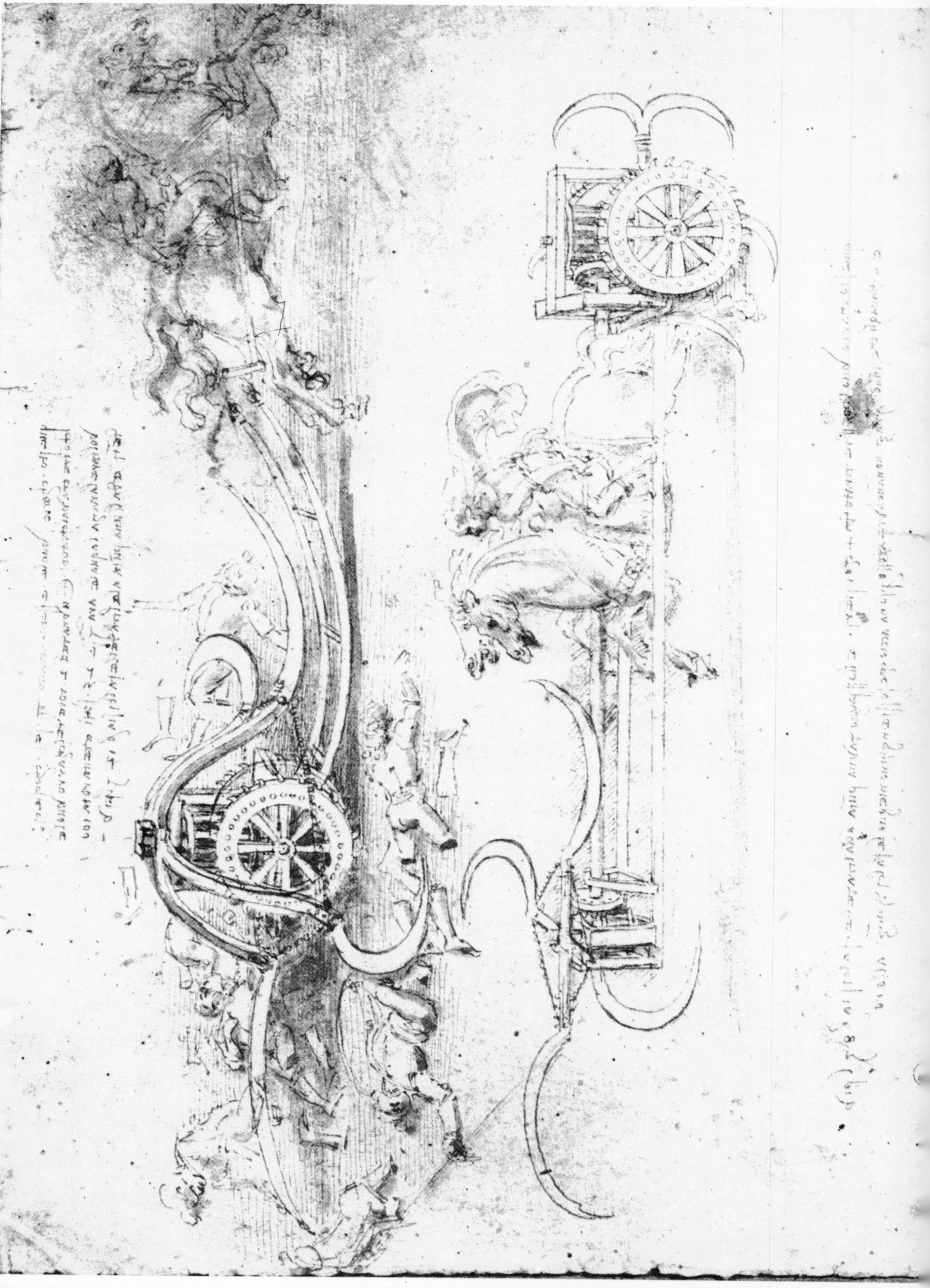

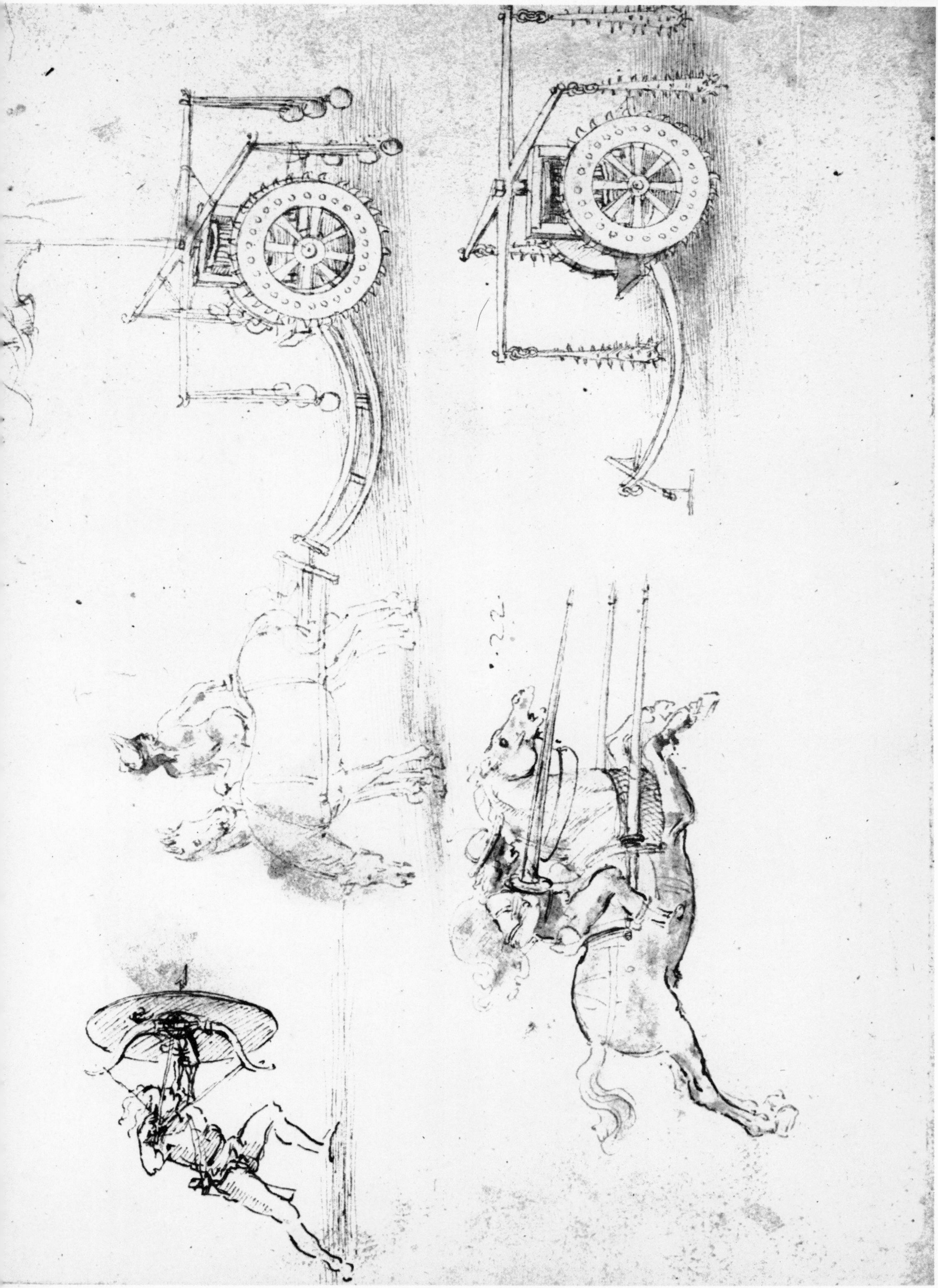

PAGE 110: Two Chariots Armed with Scythes, c. 1485–88. Pen and wash. Leonardo warned that such chariots "could do no less injury to friends than to enemies" unless properly used. As a defense he suggested "bowmen, slingers, and spearmen" who should "throw all manner of darts, spears, stones, and bombs, with beating of drums and shouting . . . and by this means you will spread panic among the horses and they will charge at their own side in frenzy." Royal Library, Turin

PAGE 111: Chariots Armed with Flails and War Clubs, a Bowman with a Shield, and a Horseman with Three Lances, c. 1485–88. Pen and ink and wash. Windsor; reproduced by gracious permission of Her Majesty the Queen

Giant Crossbow on Wheels, c. 1485–88. Pen and ink and wash. Though large *ballistae* of this type were constructed, like that in the Castel S. Angelo in Rome, it is highly unlikely that anything on this scale was ever attempted. Ambrosiana, Milan

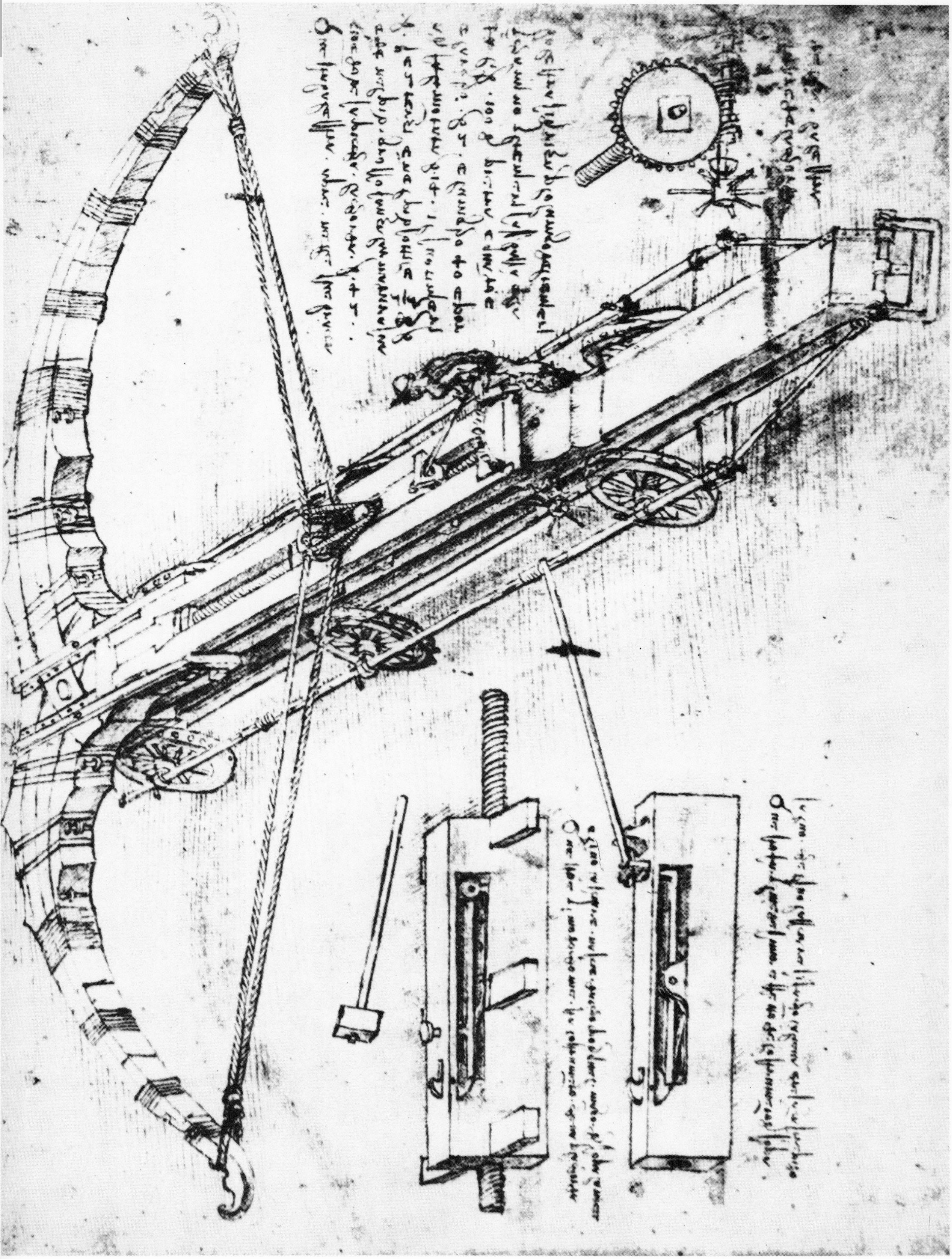

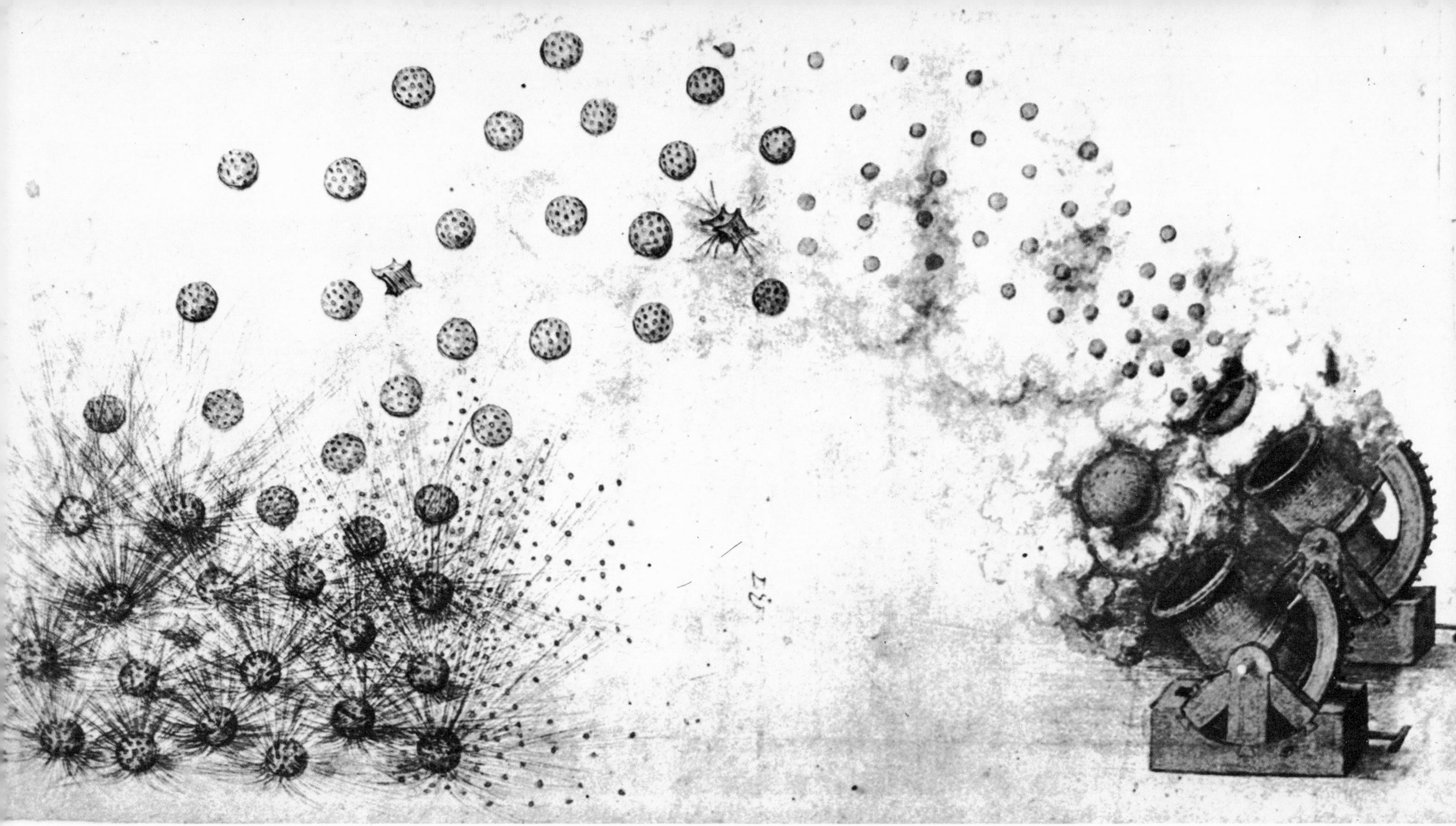

Bombards Firing Shells and Caltrops, c. 1485–88. Pen and ink and wash. The shells are filled with shrapnel, and the three jagged pieces of metal with sharp points and edges are the caltrops, so designed that however they land some of the points are upright so as to wound men and horses. Leonardo urged hurling cartloads of them with mangonels to prevent an attack. He also devised several kinds of exploding ammunition to make maximum use of the bombards' lobbing fire. Ambrosiana, Milan

Studies of Shields for Foot Soldiers and of a Bomb, c. 1485–88. Pen and ink. École des Beaux-Arts, Paris

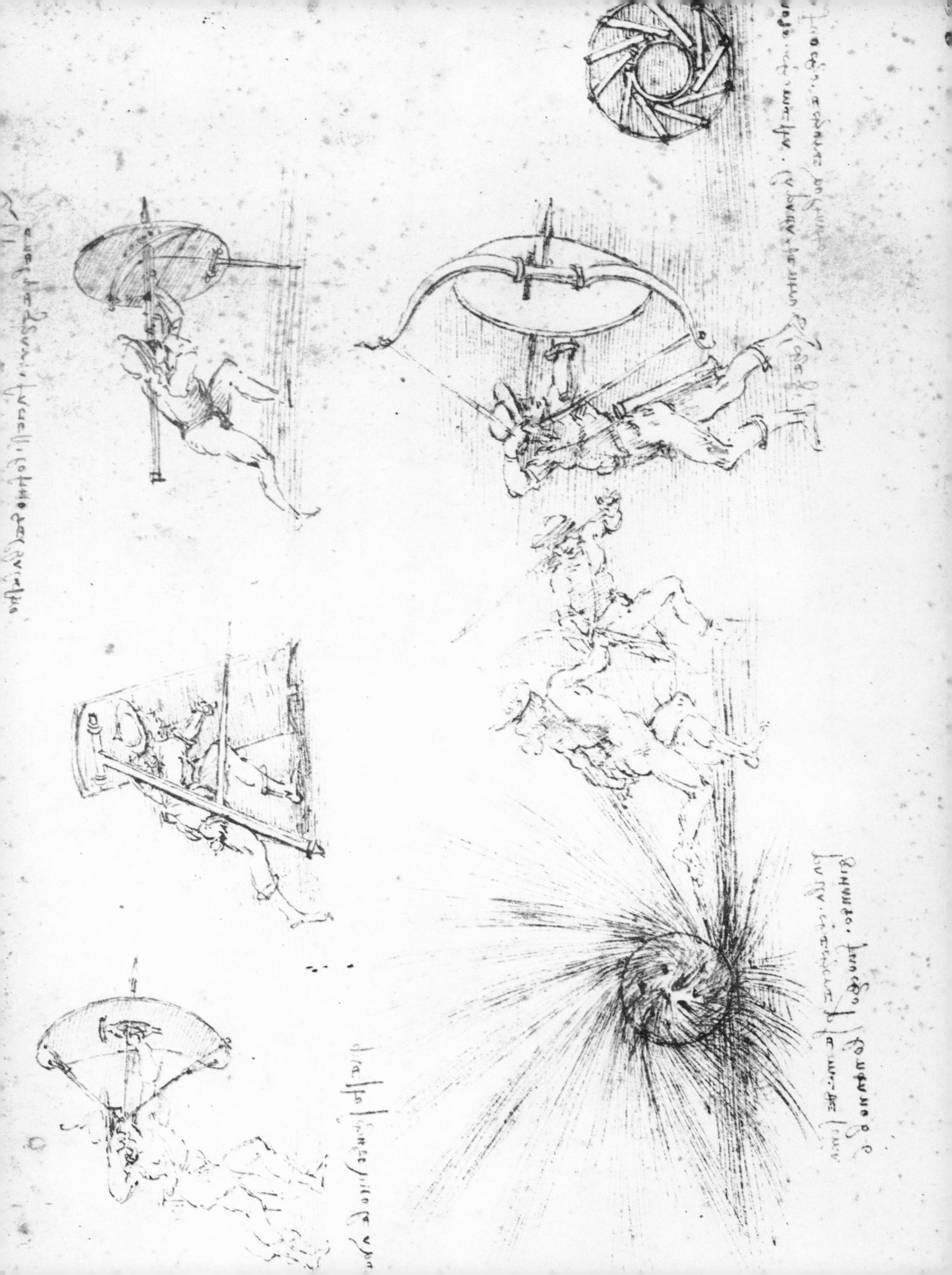

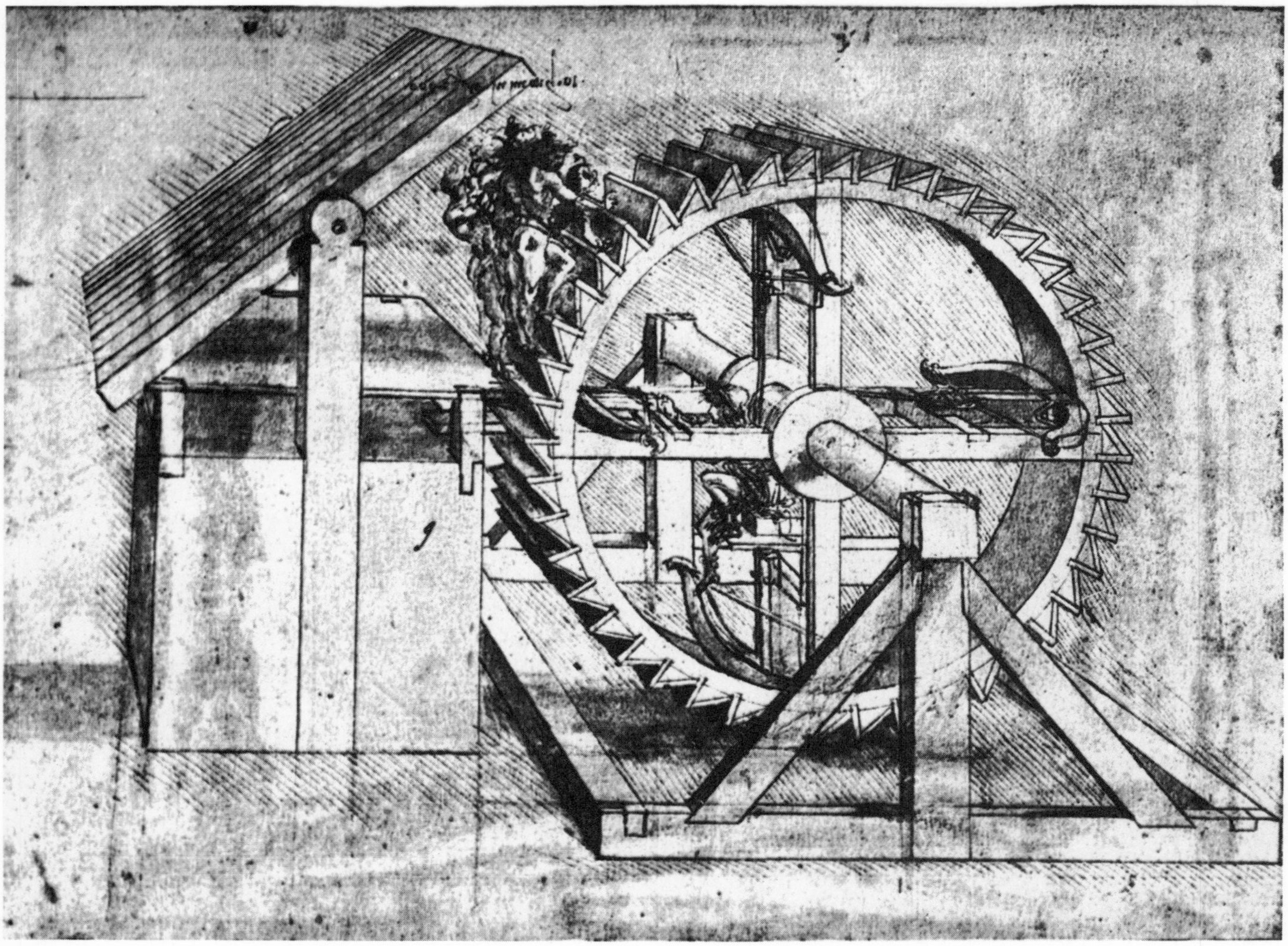

Crossbows Mounted in a Wheel, c. 1485–88. Pen and ink. Like the designs for multiple cannon, this device shows Leonardo's interest as a military engineer in increasing firepower. Ambrosiana, Milan

Two types of Catapult and a *Ballista,* c. 1485–88. Pen and ink. Leonardo knew of material fatigue because he noted that the catapult, which uses a swinging arm, "does not become exhausted as does the crossbow." Ambrosiana, Milan

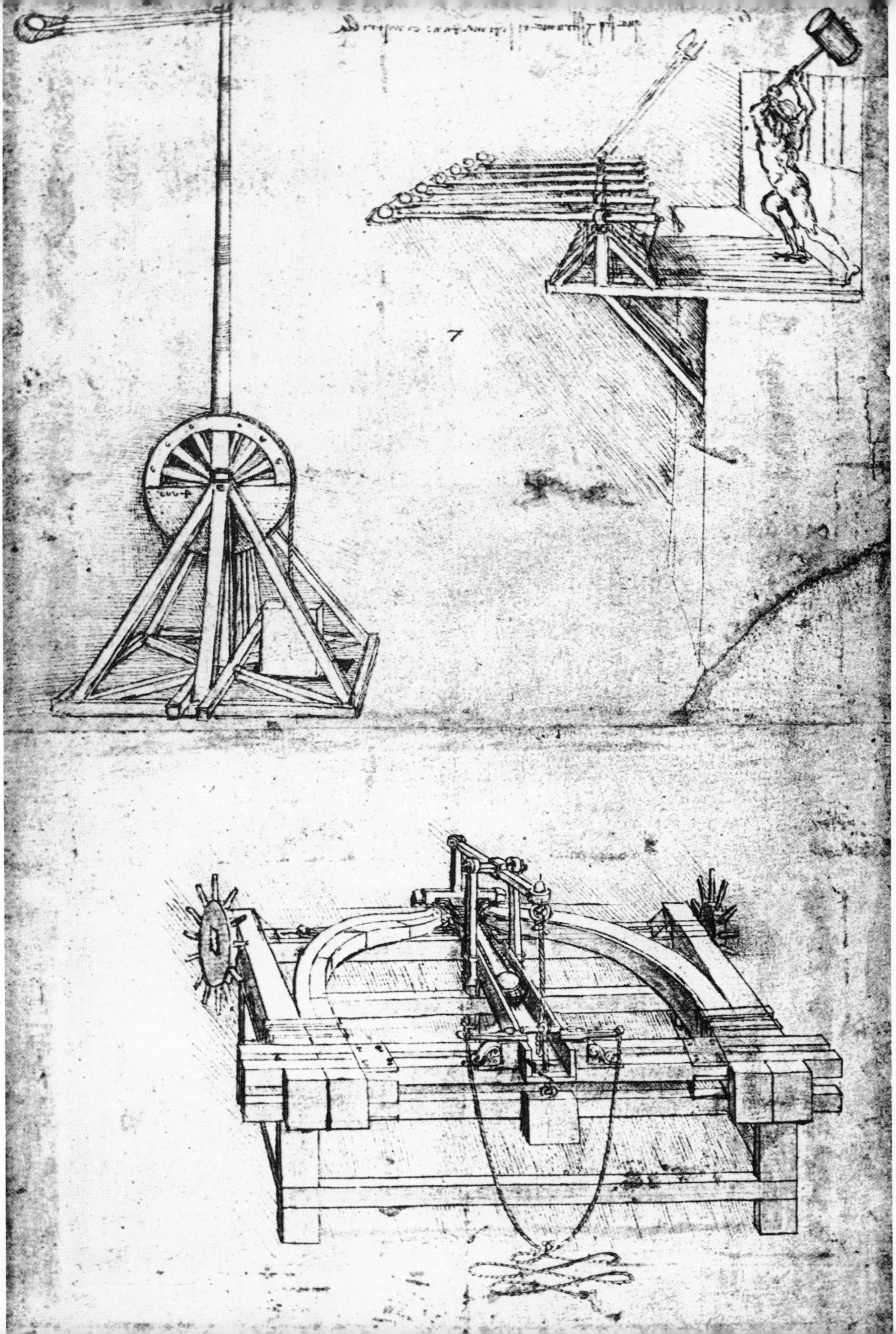
7

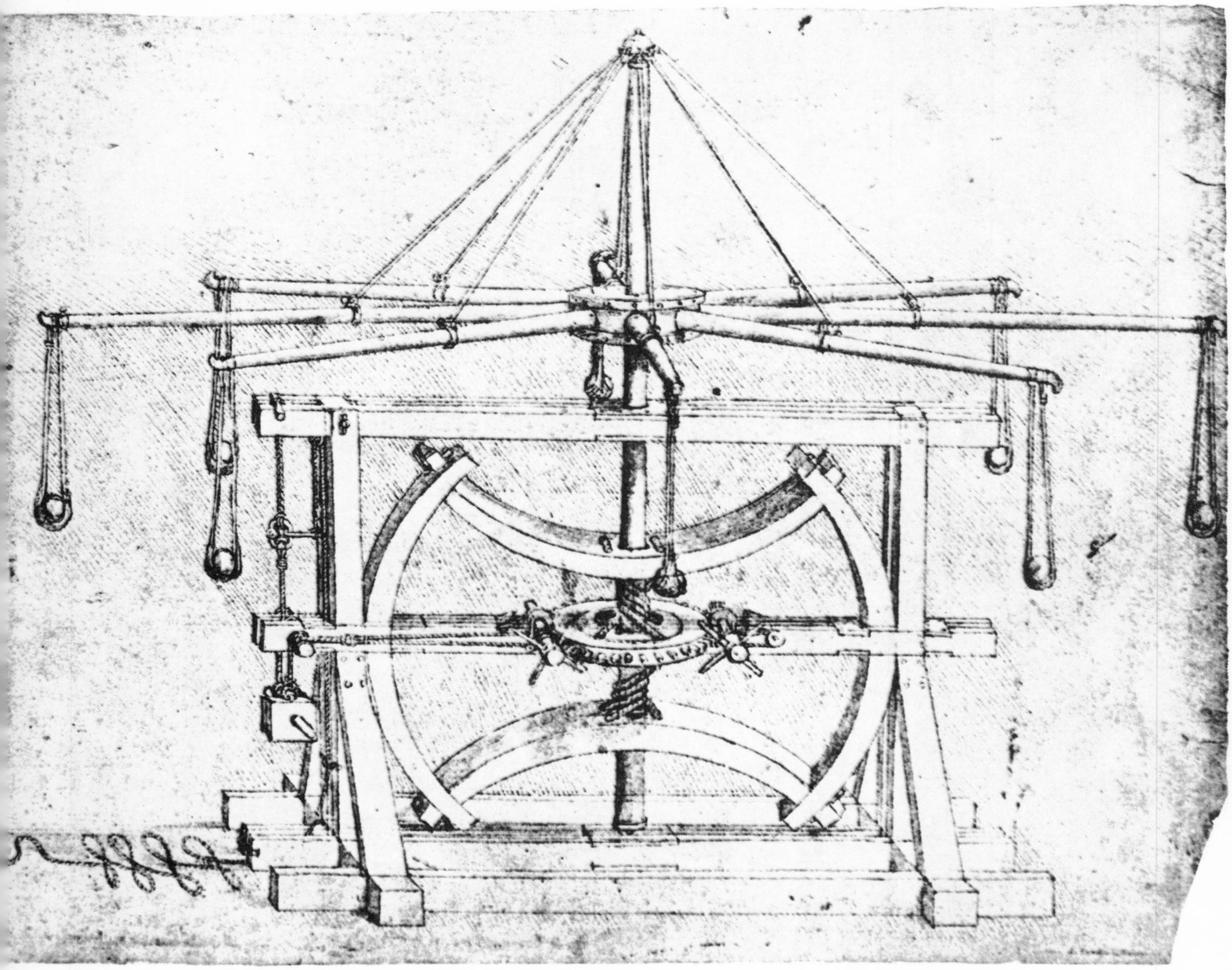

A Centrifugal Mangonel with Eight Arms, c. 1485–88. Pen and ink. Ambrosiana, Milan

A Spring Catapult, c. 1485–88. Pen and ink. Ambrosiana, Milan

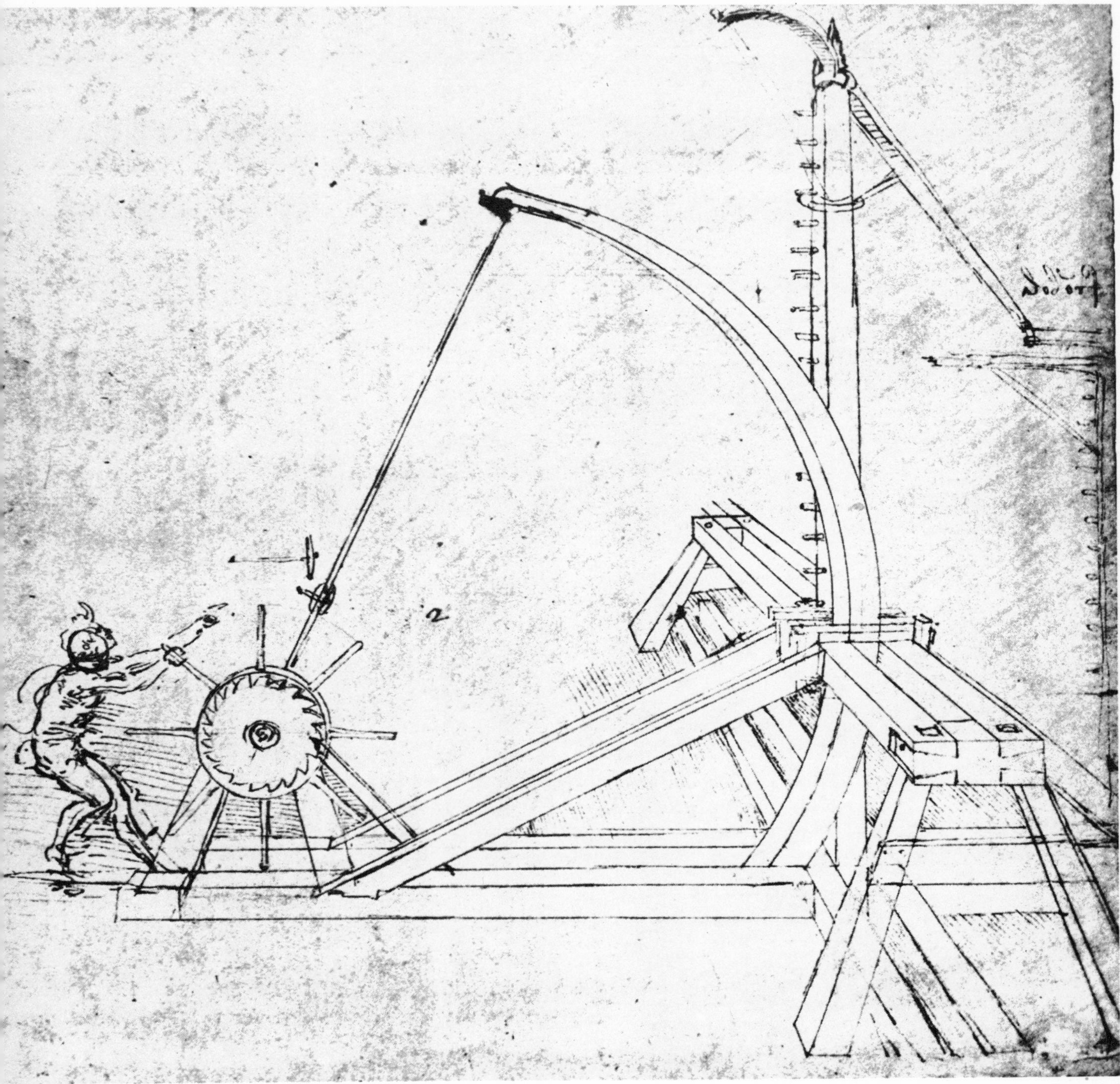
2

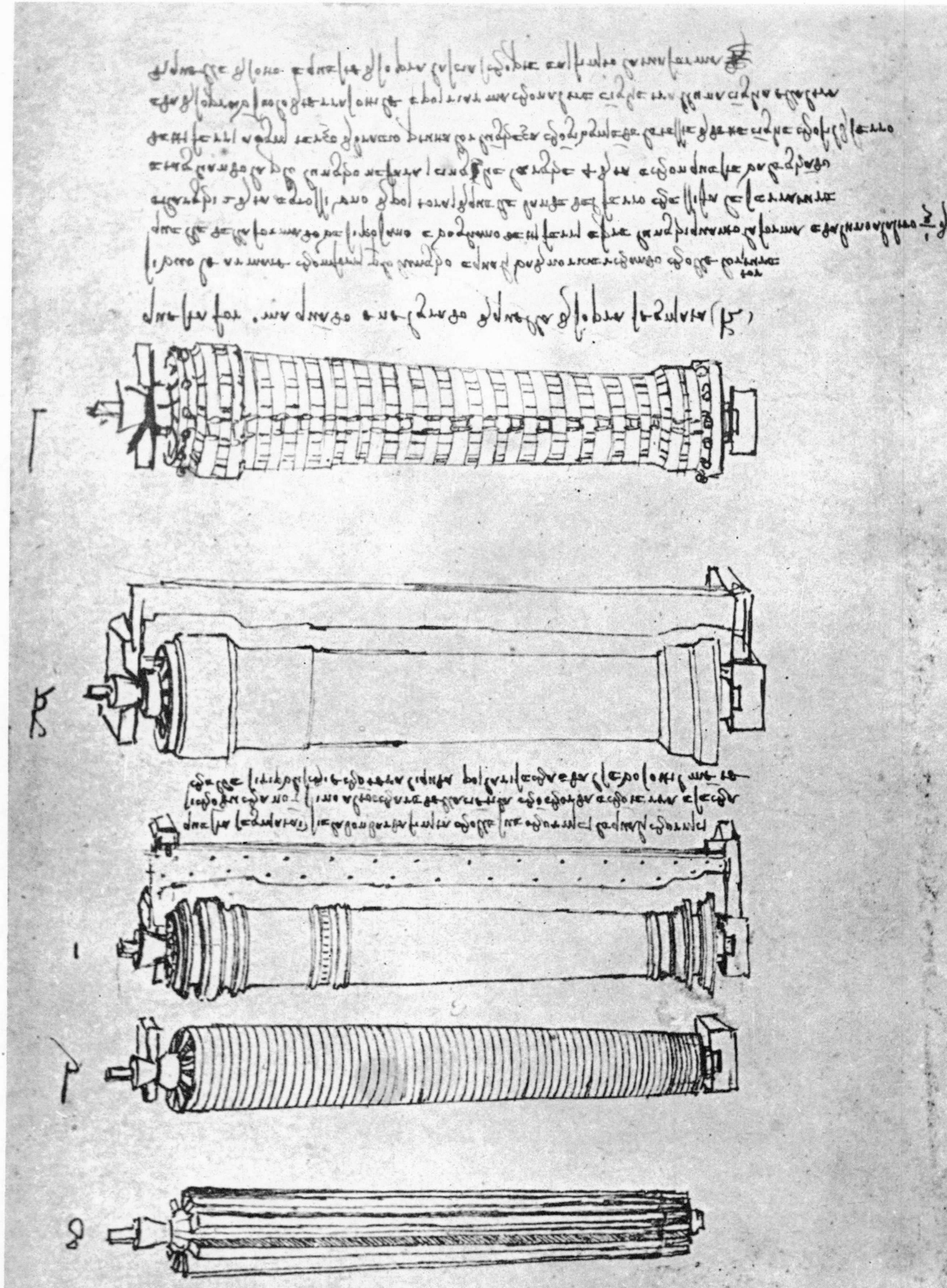

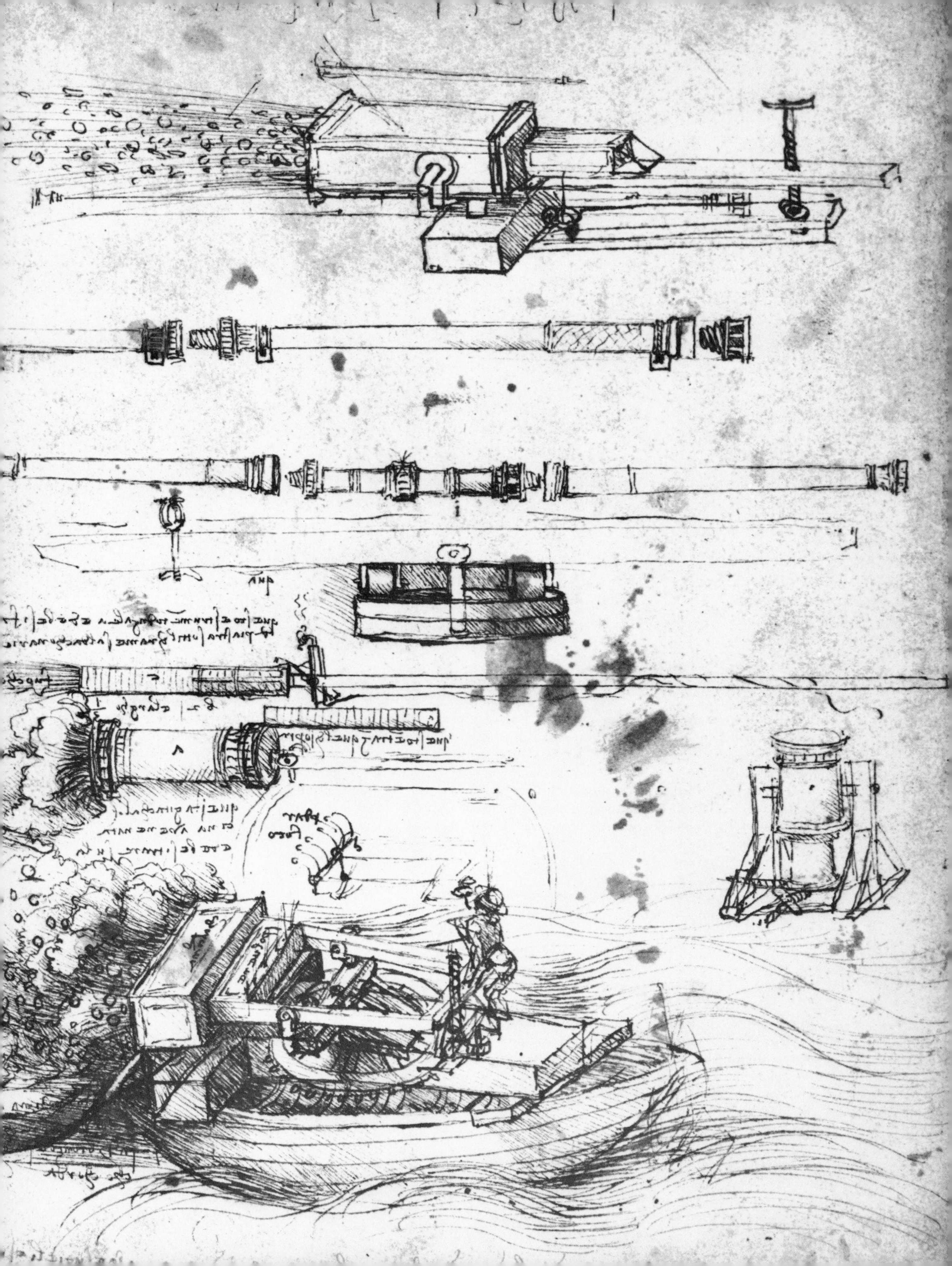

PAGE 120: Study Showing the Stages in the Construction of a Cannon, c. 1485–88. Pen and ink. Though Leonardo preferred casting, the usual method of production in his day was that illustrated here. At the top is the core, which is covered with hoops of iron in the next drawing. The staves are then set edge to edge and welded, and further hoops shrunk in place as shown at the bottom. The drawing above it shows the cannon mounted for completion with the moldings shown in the drawing above it in turn. After this stage the core was removed and the whole cleaned and polished. Ambrosiana, Milan

PAGE 121: Studies of Mortars and Cannon, c. 1485–88. Pen and ink. The various types of firearms include a small bombard at the top and a large one mounted on a boat at the bottom. Between are several cannon designed for breech loading as the screw breeches show. Two other types of bombard are being fired just above the bomb ketch, while a more familiar form, like the famous Sforza bombards, so heavy they could be moved only with winches, stands muzzle up at the right. The miscellaneous nature of the charge is suggested in the drawing. Windsor; reproduced by gracious permission of Her Majesty the Queen

Three Types of Multibarreled Cannon, c. 1485–88. Pen and ink. The one at the top has three rows of twelve barrels each attached to an axle so that, when one row is fired, another is rotated into place, and while the first cools the next is loaded. The heavy carriage is to withstand the recoil. All three use a screw device for controlling elevation. Ambrosiana, Milan

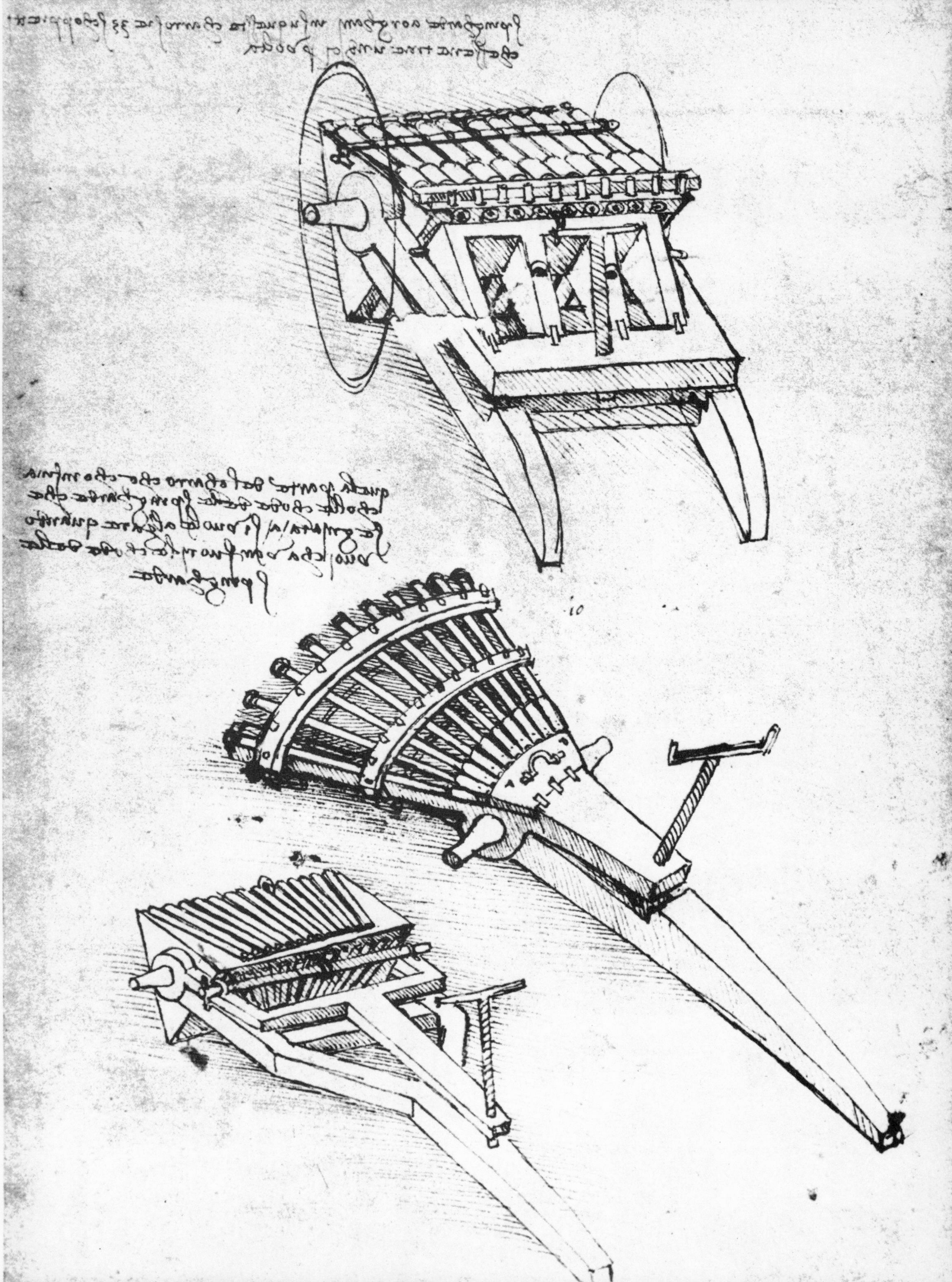

Architronito è una machina di fine rame, invenzione d'Archimede, e gitta ballotte di ferro con grande strepito e furore. E si usa in questo modo: la terza parte dello strumento sta infra gran quantità di fuoco di carboni, e quando sarà bene infocata, serra la vite d che è sopra al vaso dell'acqua a b c, e nel serrare la vite di sopra, si diserrerà di sotto, e tutta la sua acqua discenderà nella parte infocata dello strumento, e di subito si convertirà in tanto fumo che parrà maraviglia, e massime a vedere la furia e sentire lo strepito. Questa cacciava una ballotta che pesava uno talento sei stadi.

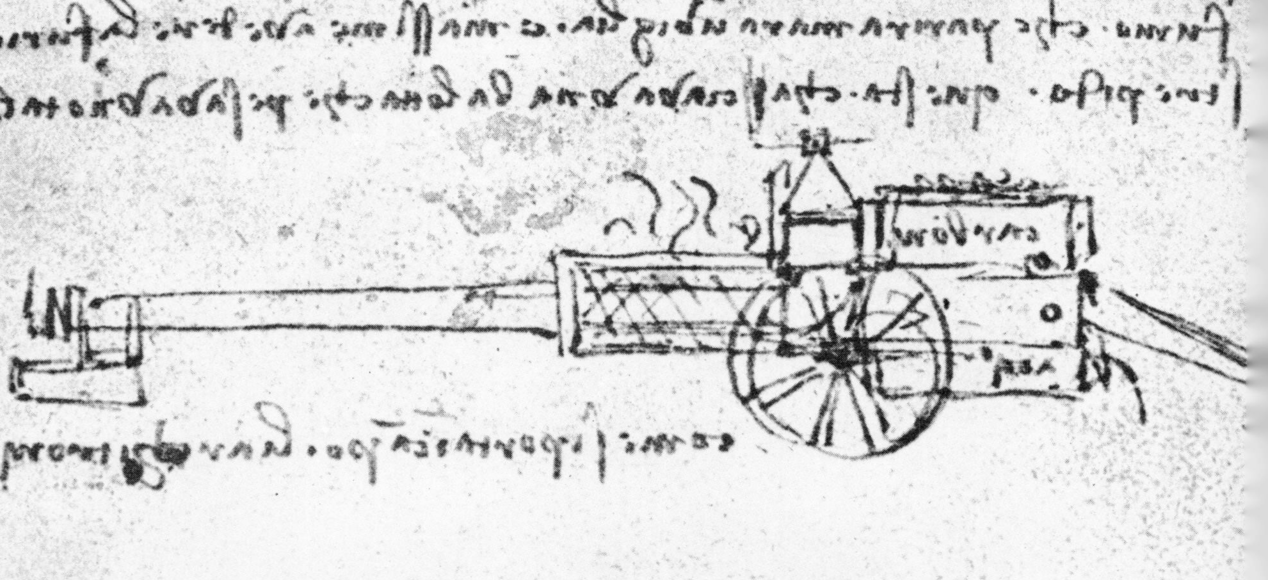

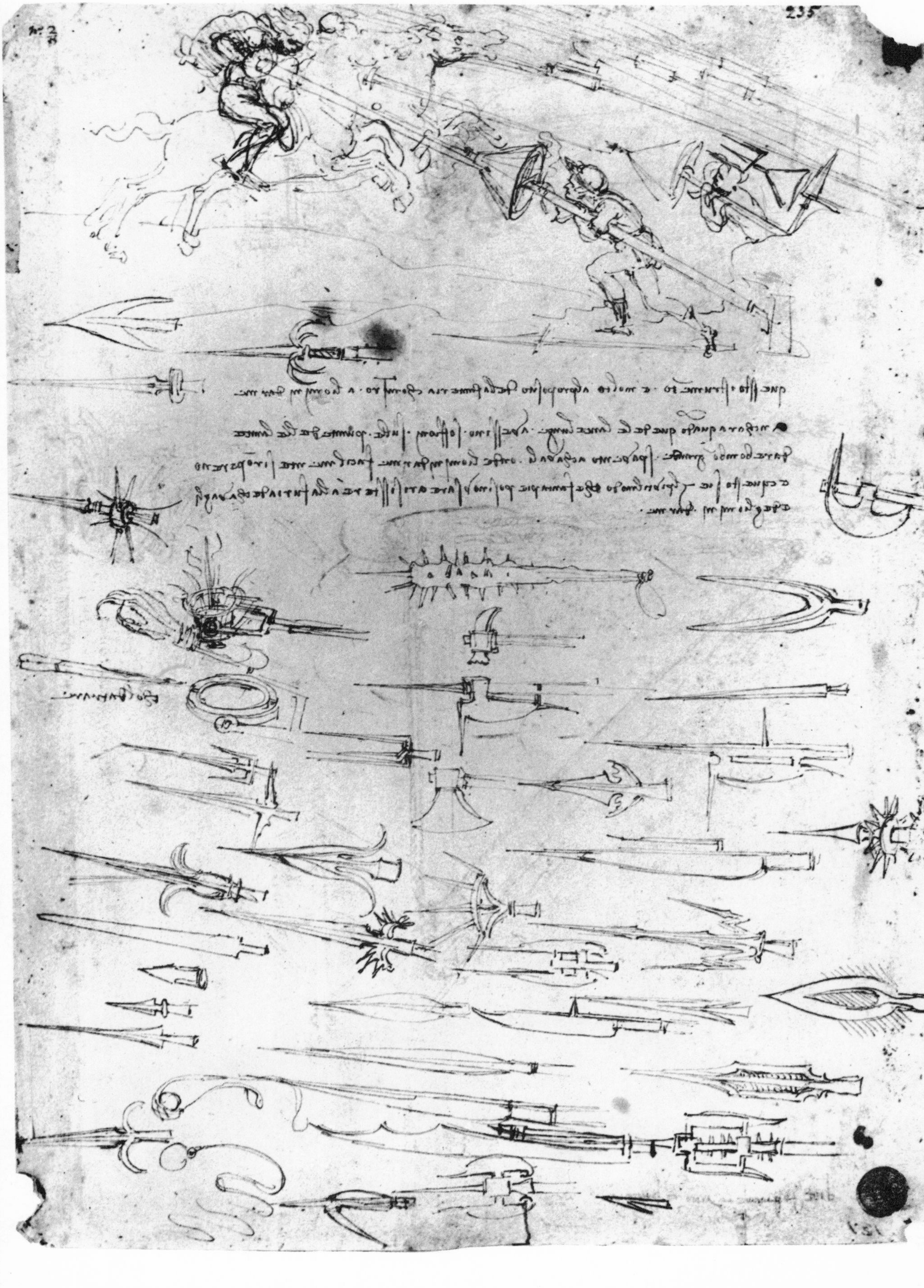

PAGE 124: The *Architronito* or Steam Cannon, c. 1485–88. Pen and ink. "The *architronito,*" Leonardo wrote, "throws iron balls with a great noise and fury. . . . The third part of the instrument stands within a great quantity of burning coals, and when it has been thoroughly heated by these," a turn of the screw "which is above the cistern of water," allows the water to "descend into the heated part of the machine, and there it will instantly become changed into so much steam that it will seem marvelous, and especially when one sees its fury and hears its roar." Institut de France, Paris

PAGE 125: Foot Soldiers with Shielded Lances Attacking Horsemen, and Various Weapons, c. 1485–88. Pen and ink. Academy, Venice

Assault Ladders, c. 1485–88. Pen and ink. One of the soldiers at the bottom is using pitons, like those employed by mountain climbers, forced into cracks in the masonry. "When you are at the top, fix the rope ladder . . . and cause the assailants to ascend quickly," Leonardo advised. Ambrosiana, Milan

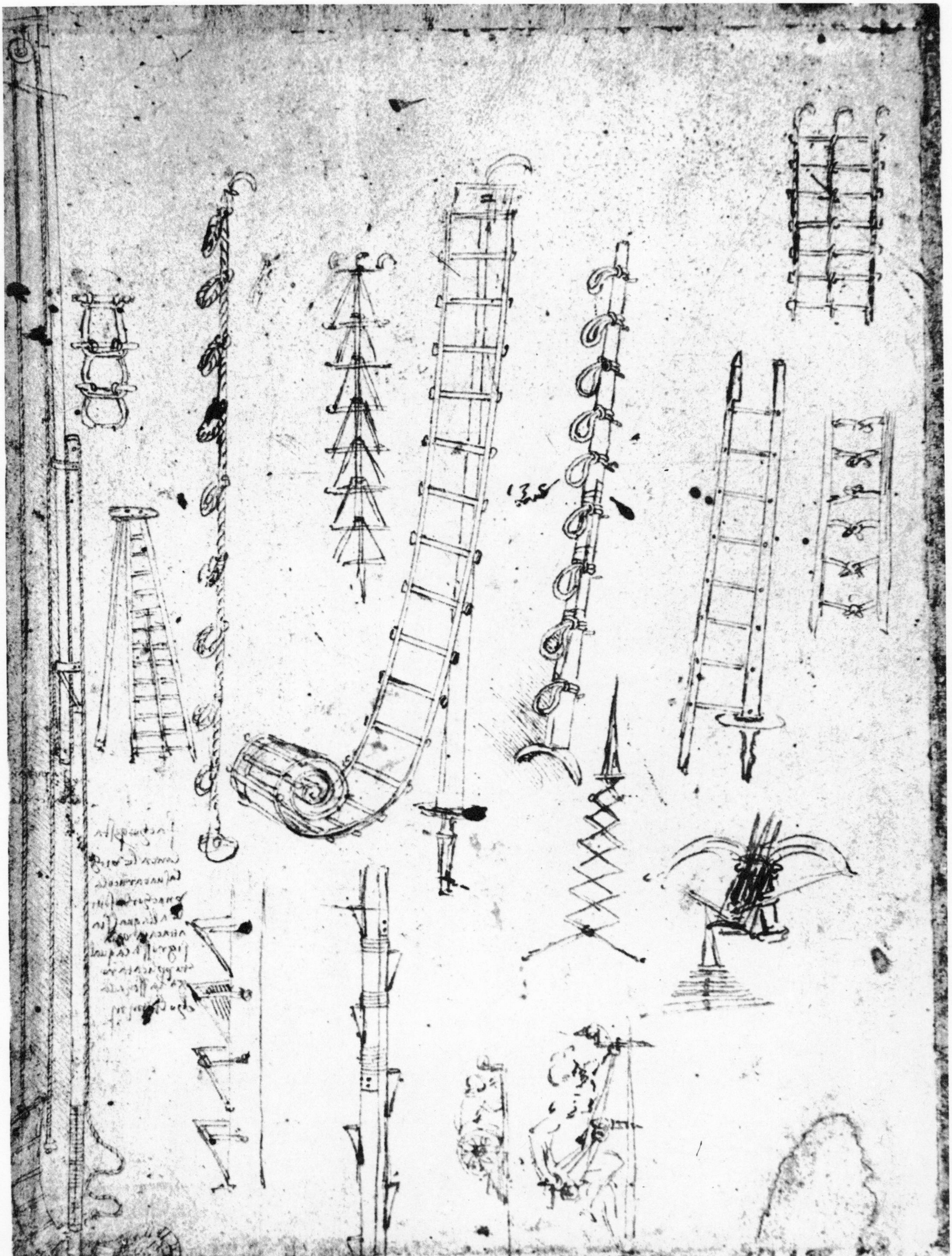

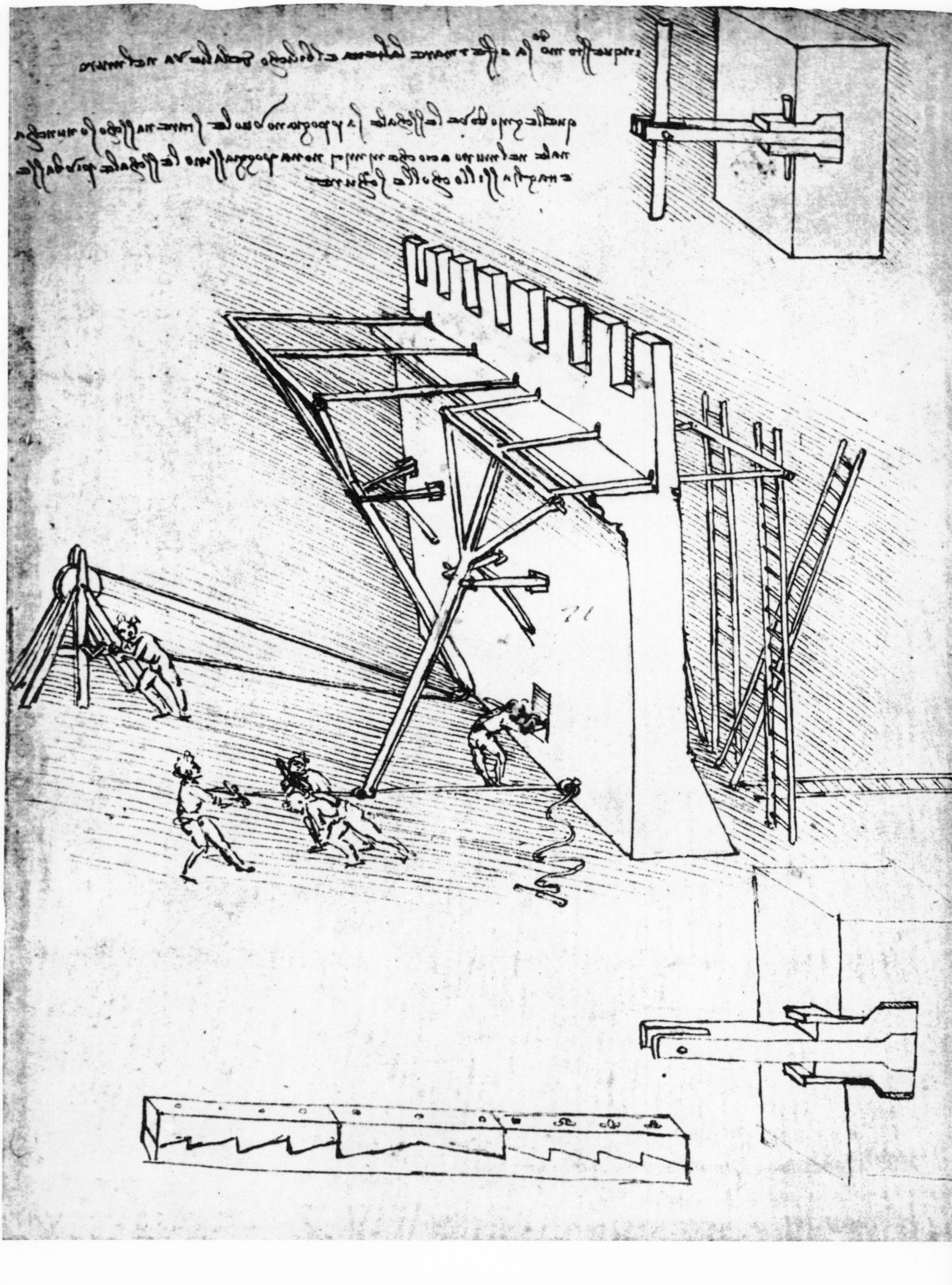

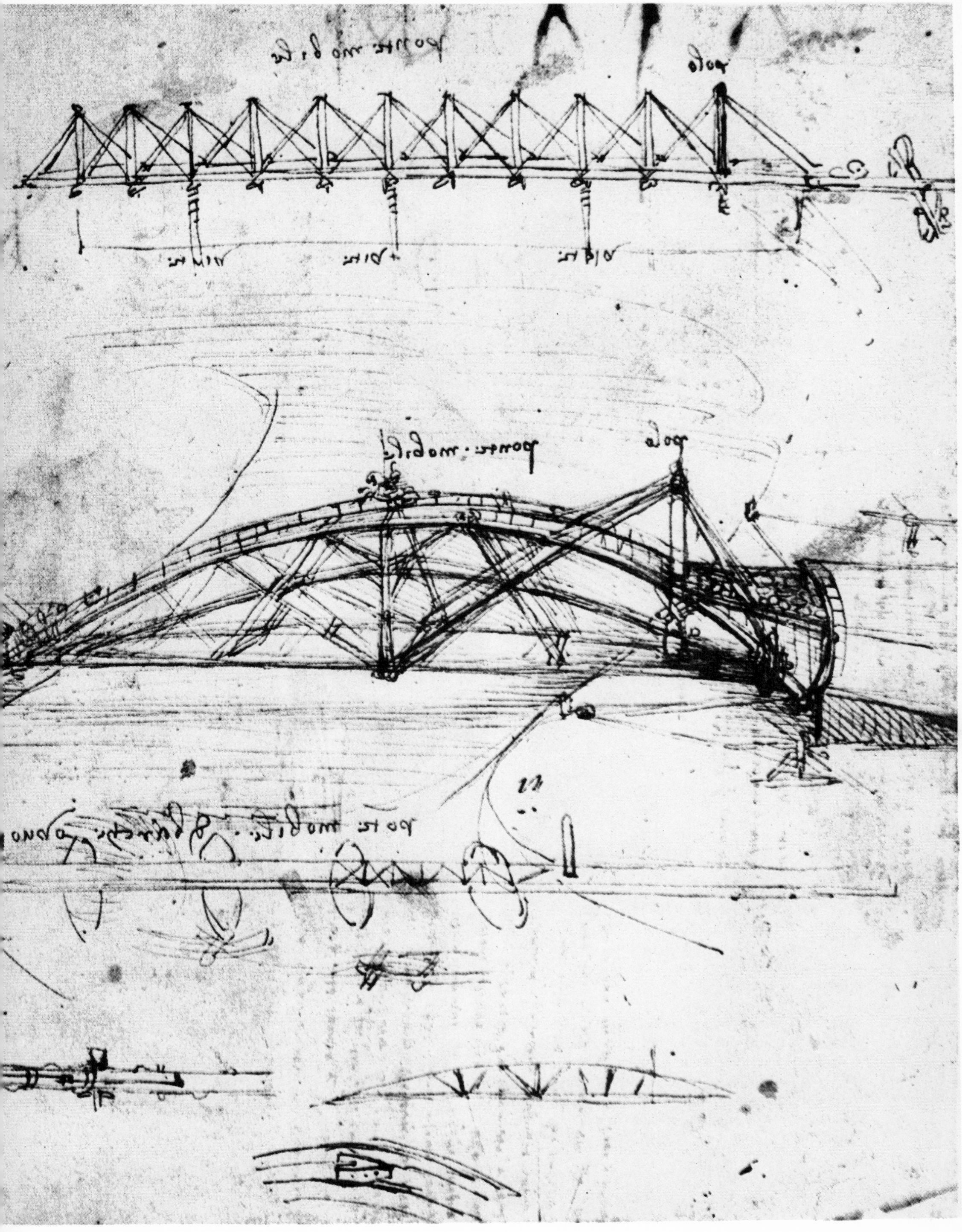

PAGE 128: A Device for Repelling Scaling Ladders, c. 1475–80. Pen and ink. Two details show how to fasten it to a masonry wall, and at the bottom is a sketch of a scarf joint for connecting heavy pieces of wood. Ambrosiana, Milan

PAGE 129: Three Types of Swinging Bridge, c. 1485. Pen and ink. The one at the top carries the walkway by a suspension system. That in the center is pivoted at the right, and swung by pulleys and capstans to perform a similar function to that of a drawbridge. Below is a sketch of a swinging pontoon bridge. Ambrosiana, Milan

A Siege Tower, c. 1485–88. Pen and ink. The tower was to be moved into place by oxen so that its covered bridge could be lowered onto the enemy battlements, as in the drawing. Ambrosiana, Milan

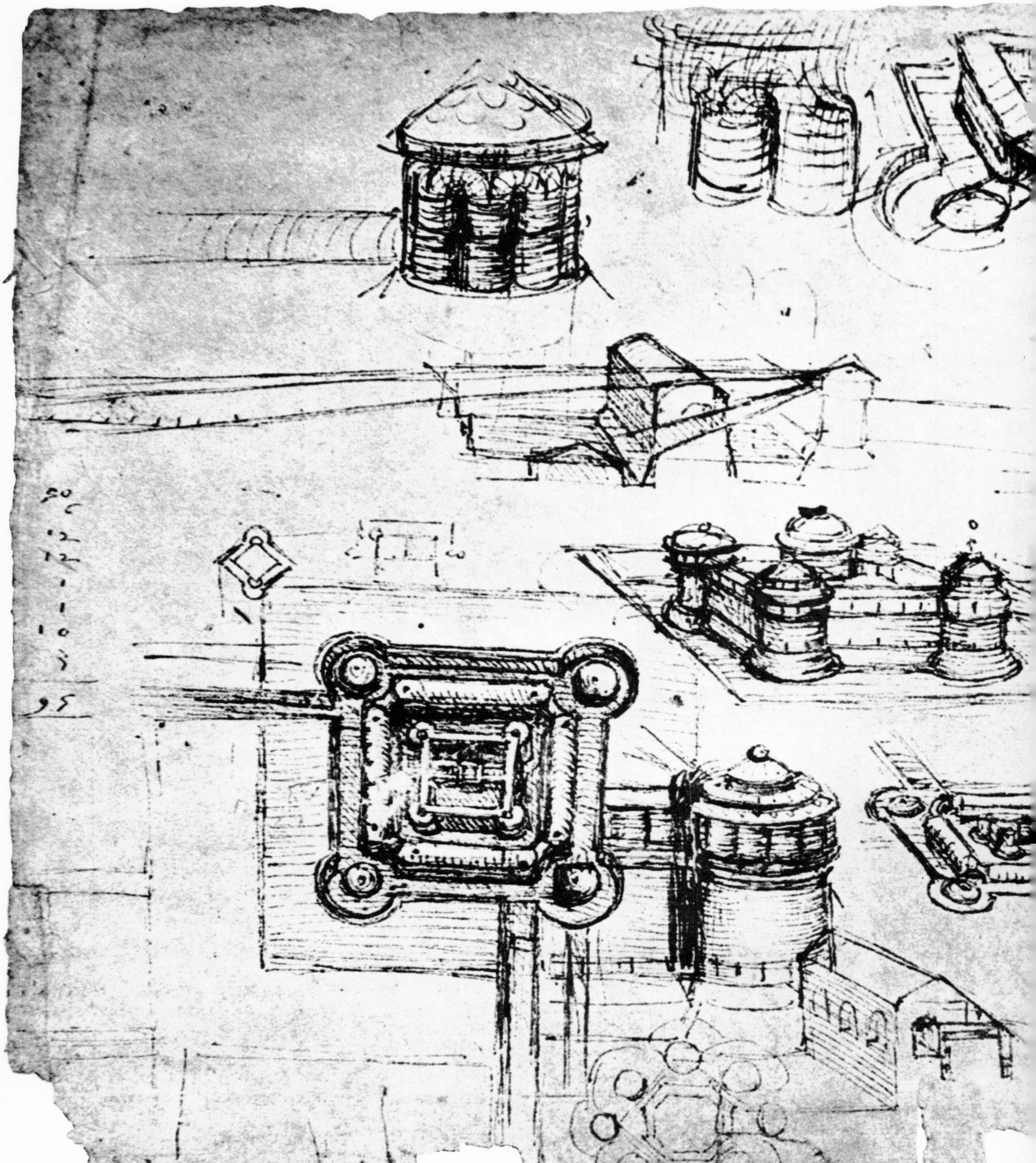

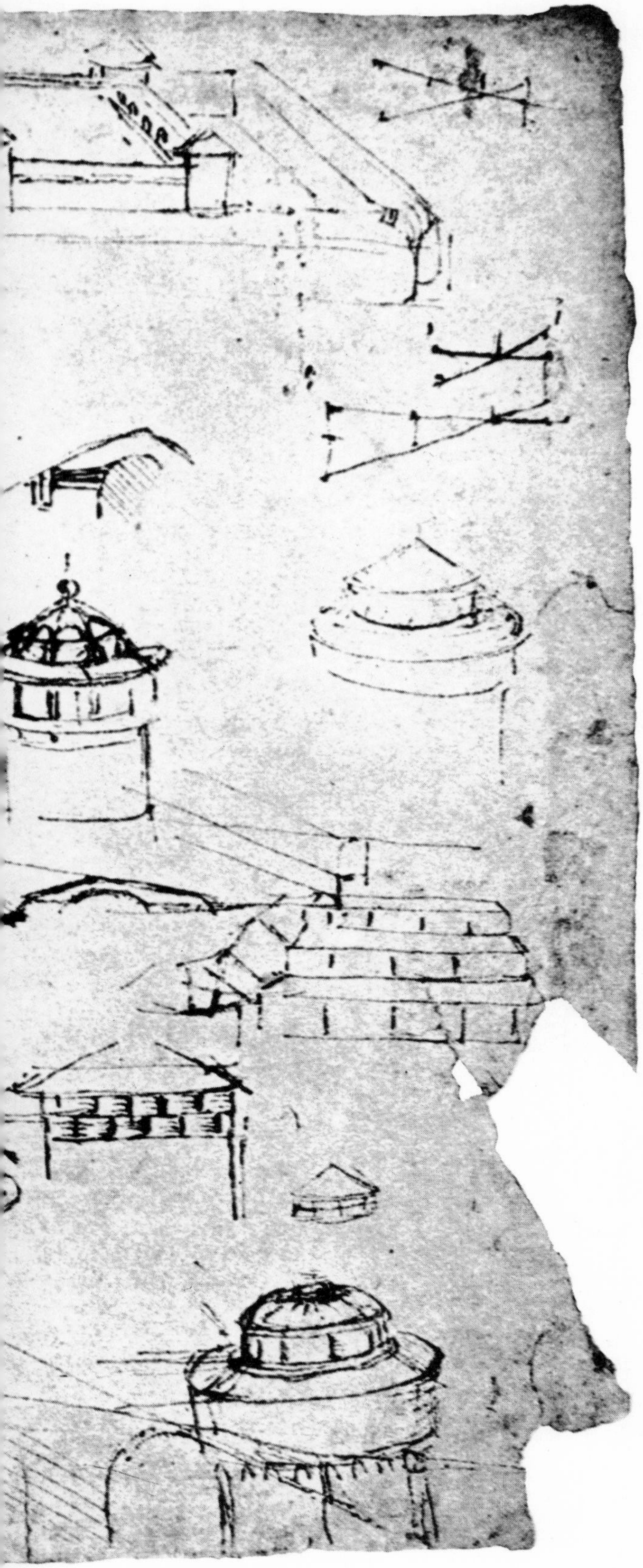

Drawings of Fortifications, c. 1485–88. Pen and ink. Here Leonardo suggests the new approach to fortification necessitated by the development of artillery, rounding the forms and surfaces to deflect the shot, lowering and thickening the walls with the inner defenses higher so that their fire can cover the lower outer works. At lower left is a plan for a fortress of three concentered square defenses and four corner towers, each separated from the rest by moats, and joined only by subterranean passages which could be flooded if outer portions were captured. Ambrosiana, Milan

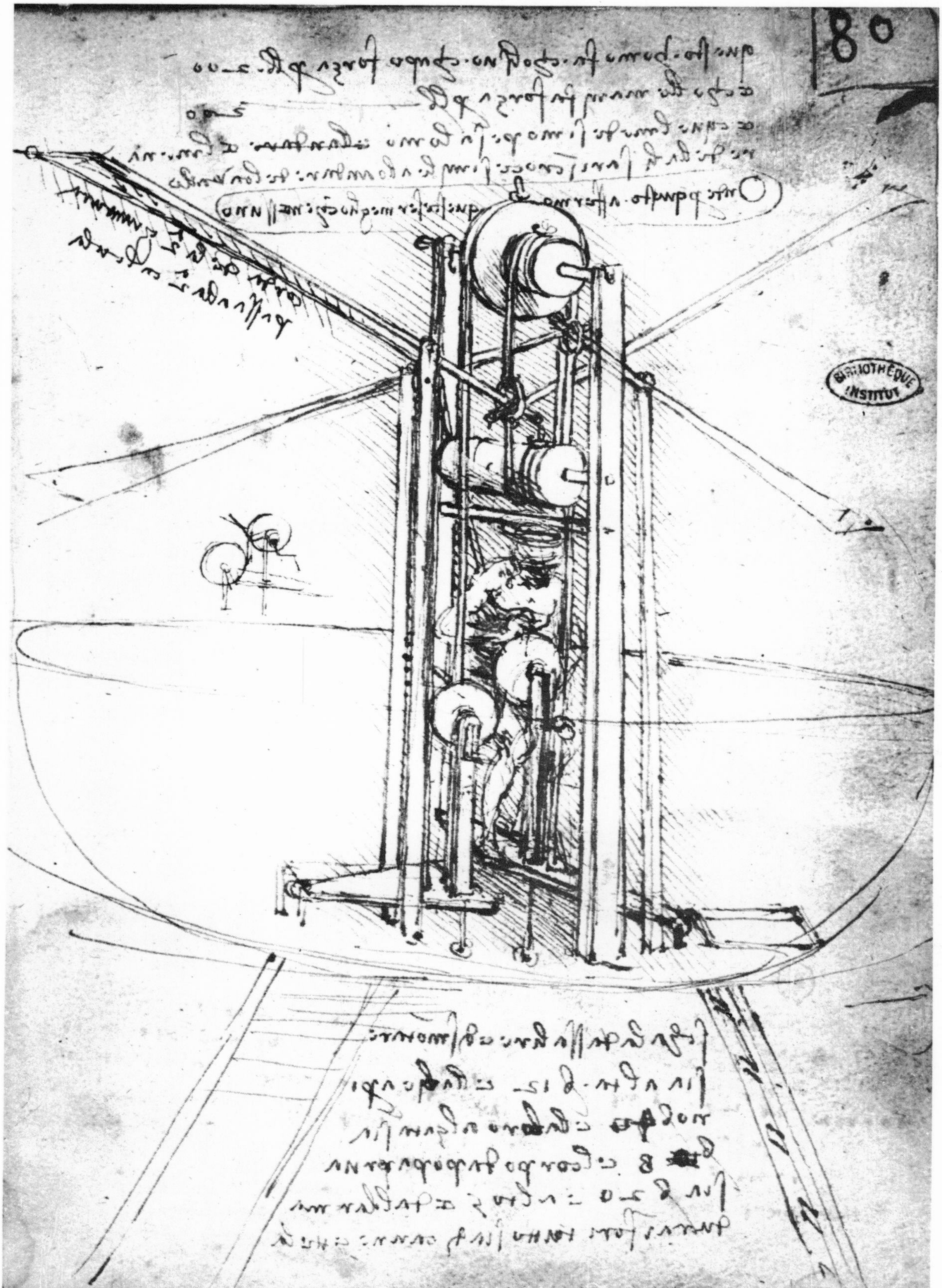
80
BIBLIOTHÈQUE INSTITUT

"The Great Bird Will Take Its Flight"

Conquest of the air is an age-old dream of man which fascinated Leonardo, and his notes *On the Flight of Birds* are among the most complete he ever wrote and form the first systematic analysis of the principles of flight. They are full of his quick-eyed observation and consider both flapping and soaring flight, the importance of the center of gravity for aerial stability, the pressures of the air on wing surfaces, and "the science of the winds," many of the points being illustrated with swift sketches. He studied the structure and articulation of the wings of birds, noting the pulleylike action of muscles and tendons on the upstroke, which is reflected in some of the mechanisms he designed. "Dissect the bat," he wrote, "and concentrate on this, and on this model arrange the machine." He refers again and again to "the bird," a flying machine with movable wings designed like those of "the bat, because membranes form a framework . . . which binds the whole and is not pierced." He drew a number of studies of wings of this pattern, and made tests to determine the force needed to move those large enough to support a man. He even conceived an additional small wing for use as a kind of air brake and to assist in maneuvering in a way suggesting the function of wing flaps on a modern plane.

The first designs of flying machines show the operator prone in a harness which allows him to activate the wings and use the feet for added control. For some years Leonardo thought it possible to design a mechanism that a man could fly through the use of the power of his arms alone, and he made many studies of various arrangements of levers and pulleys for this purpose. He constantly strove to lighten and strengthen the structure, trying out all kinds of available materials: laminated fir or hemlock, springs of laminated steel or horn, and hinges of leather, alum-tanned for strength and resiliency. After he returned to Florence in 1503 he turned to other ideas, some to take advantage of the greater strength of a man's legs, and he designed several machines in which the operator was to be in an upright position. One had its own platform for taking off and landing, while another, with four wings, was to be flown by two men.

Finally he conceived the helicopter, a kind of aerial application of the screw as in the airplane propeller, and a parachute. He described the latter as "a tent made of linen of which the apertures have all been stopped up, and it is twelve

---

Drawing of a Flying Machine with Operator, c. 1500. Pen and ink. Institut de France, Paris

ells across and twelve in depth," with which a man "will be able to throw himself down from a great height without any injury." Only in these two cases did he depart from the theory of flapping flight, despite the fact that his studies of birds were more and more, as time went on, observations of the gliding action which was to provide the principle of the fixed-wing flight of the airplane. There seems no evidence that he concerned himself with the lighter-than-air flight of balloons. His identification with nature was so complete that he believed sufficient study and understanding of natural principles would provide a way. Just as man could swim in the sea, he believed he could conquer the air, not by blasting through it with awkward violence as in today's airplanes, but in silent, natural flight, achieved through his own powers used according to nature's principles. It has been reported that in 1936 a young American aviator dropped from a plane, sustained himself in the air, and landed safely, through the use of a pair of movable wings. Thus, though Leonardo's helicopter was to some extent an ancestor of flight, his other

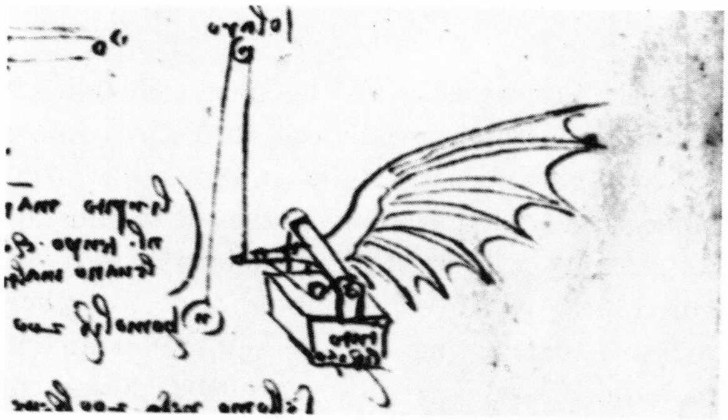

A Wing on a Test Block, c. 1490. Pen and ink. Institut de France, Paris

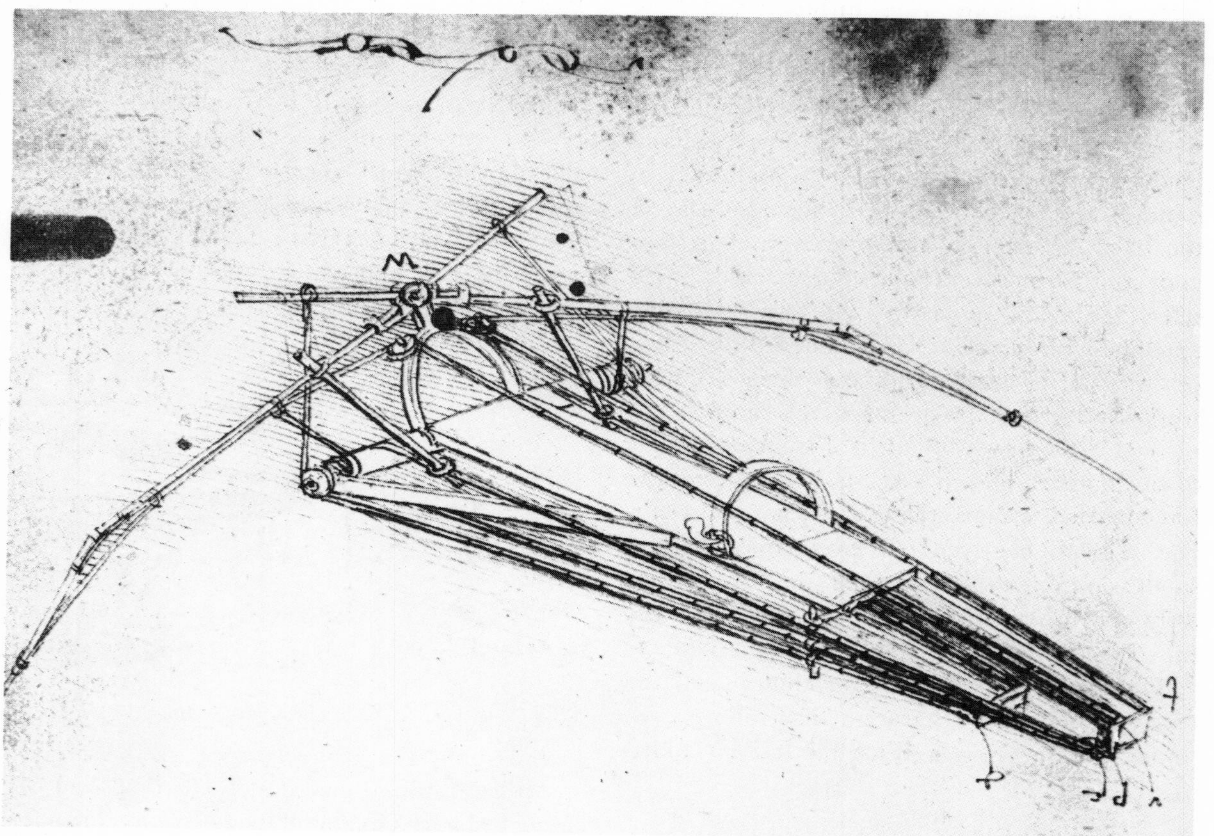

A Flying Machine, c. 1490. Pen and ink. Leonardo intended the aviator to lie prone and work the wings, whose main ribs are shown, with his feet through the stirrups, the right foot for a downward thrust, and the left to raise them. The wings are pivoted above the pilot's head, and their action was apparently to be assisted while maneuvering by the use of the arms. Institut de France, Paris

ideas for flying machines have so far had few if any successful descendants.

The principle of the parachute, however, is entirely sound, though it was not until 1783 that there is a sure record of its actual use, when a daring Frenchman named Lenormand descended safely from the top of the observatory in Montpellier in this way. The modern counterpart of Leonardo's is merely a refinement and perfection of his design, and today, in addition to being a life-saving device, it returns space capsules to earth and has become an element of offensive warfare.

There is an ancient legend that the old women of Fiesole, just north of Florence, still tell their grandchildren, of a huge bird that rose from the top of Monte Ceceri, "the mountain of the great swan," and that it disappeared, never to be seen again. There is no evidence that Leonardo actually ever tried to fly, though he certainly never lost his belief that human flight was possible, and the sentence at the very end of the pages *On the Flight of Birds* remains, part prophecy and part hope, a poignant proof of his belief.

The great bird will first take flight from the back of the great swan, filling the universe with amazement, and all writings with its fame, and bringing eternal glory to the nest where it was born.

The dream of flight, like so many other ideas of Leonardo, had to wait for centuries for realization. Yet he must have felt some of the implications of liberation from the earth, of the new and strange relations assumed by familiar things when seen from a bird's-eye view with a clarity like that of modern aerial photography. The maps which he drew show this other dimension, just as do the cosmic backgrounds of such paintings as *The Virgin and Child with St. Anne* and the *Mona Lisa.*

It was the early balloonists who first actually saw this view of the world, a long line of intrepid explorers of the air from the first flight of the brothers Joseph and Étienne Montgolfier six thousand feet above Annonay on a bright spring day in 1783. By 1808, in England, Sir George Cayley was successfully testing a glider of his own design as big as a World War II fighter. But it was not until one bitter cold morning in December of 1903, at Kitty Hawk, North Carolina, that two visionary young bicycle mechanics, Wilbur and Orville Wright, achieved a moment of powered flight, and history began a new chapter. On the four hundredth anniversary of Leonardo's birth Henri Giffard made the first successful motor-driven flight in history, from Paris to Trappes, in a dirigible, and on the five hundredth, the world's first jet airliner, the DeHavilland Comet, went into transatlantic service.

Again war, "that bestial madness," had speeded mechanical progress; it was the hectic technological experiments of wartime that catapulted the world into the jet age, and the threat of war that has pushed it into space. But in the meantime thousands of passengers cross the continents and the seas every day by air, and soon even more will be doing so at twice and more the speed of sound, while far below them small planes search the waters to direct the trawler fleets to schools of fish. Farmers' crops are dusted. Helicopters direct traffic, patrol the forests for fires, and serve as air taxis and ambulances. Suburbanites are putting together kits to make rotary planes, rather like air-borne motor scooters, small enough to park in the family garage; while soldiers in training are hovering above the trees for reconnaissance or jumping over fences and buildings by means of jet capsules strapped to their backs. After more than five centuries, Leonardo's dream of flight has become a reality of everyday life.

Drawing of a Flying Machine, c. 1490. Pen and ink. In this machine the thrust of the pilot's legs, aided by the arms, was to move the wings. "Observe how the beating of its wings against the air suffices to bear up the weight of the eagle," Leonardo wrote. "Observe also how the air moving over the sea, beaten back by the bellying sails, causes the heavily laden ship to glide onward. So that by adducing and expounding the reason for these things you may be able to realize that man when he has great wings attached to him, by exerting his strength against the resistance of the air and conquering it, is enabled to subdue it and raise himself upon it." Ambrosiana, Milan

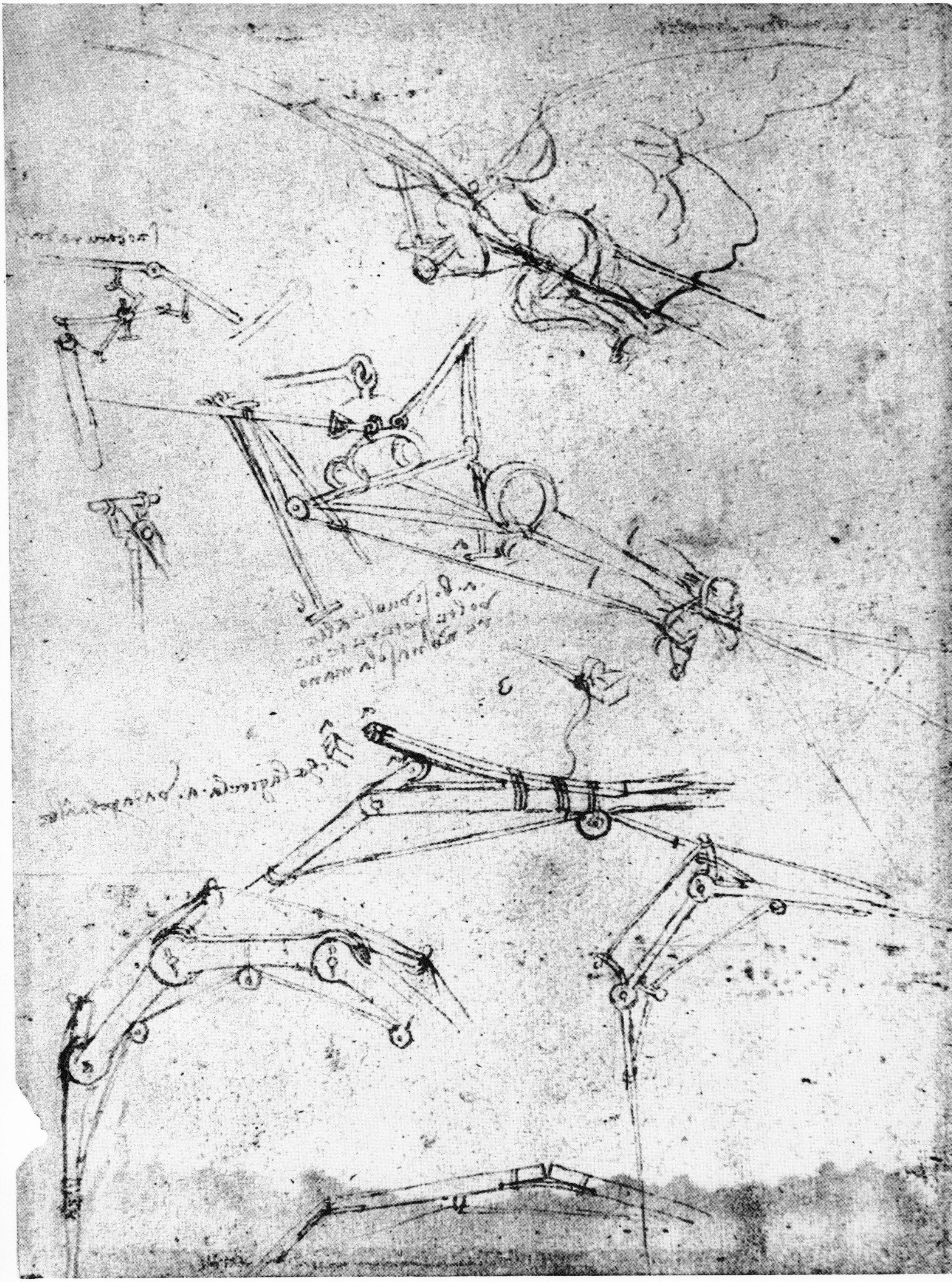

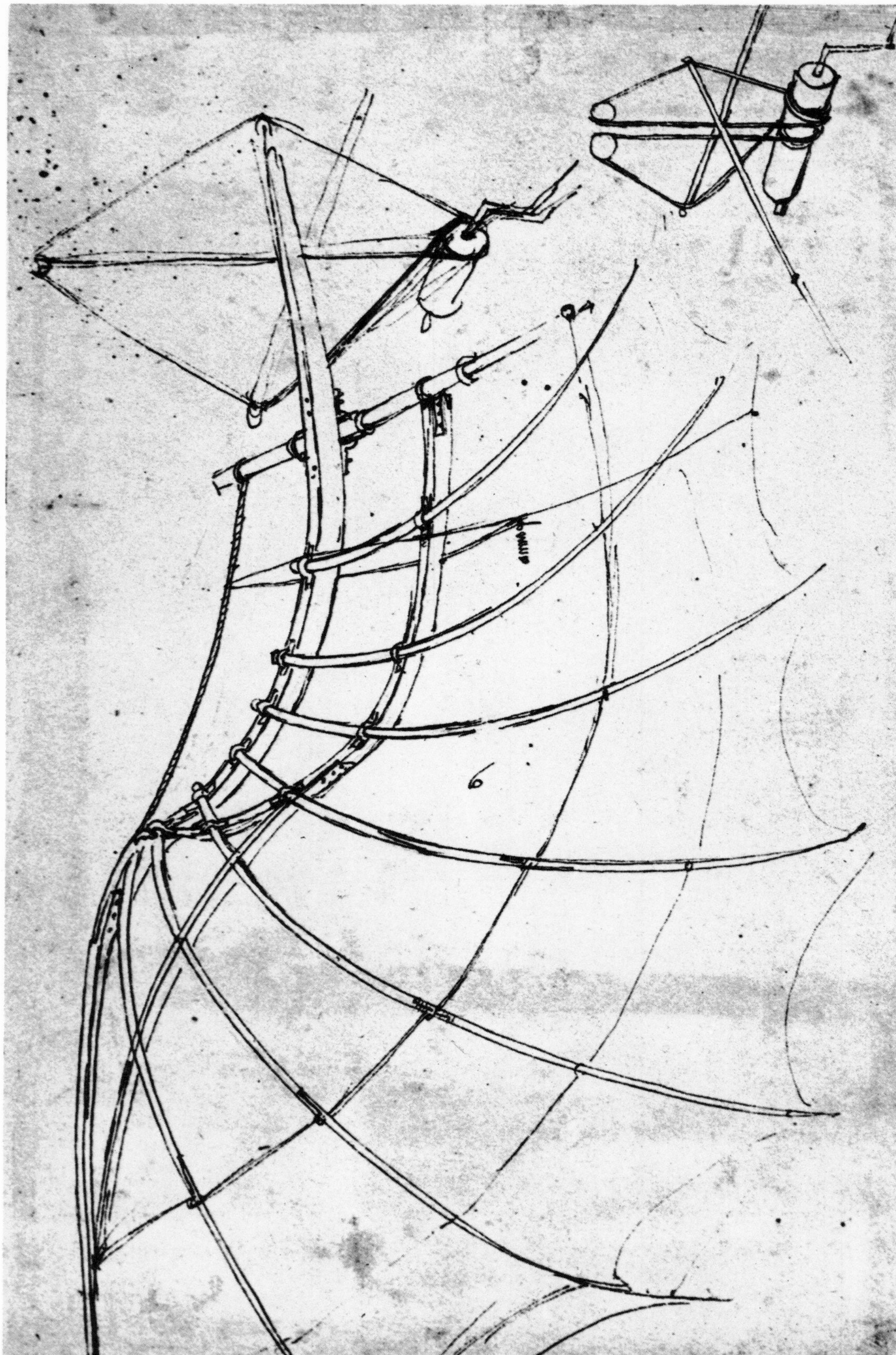

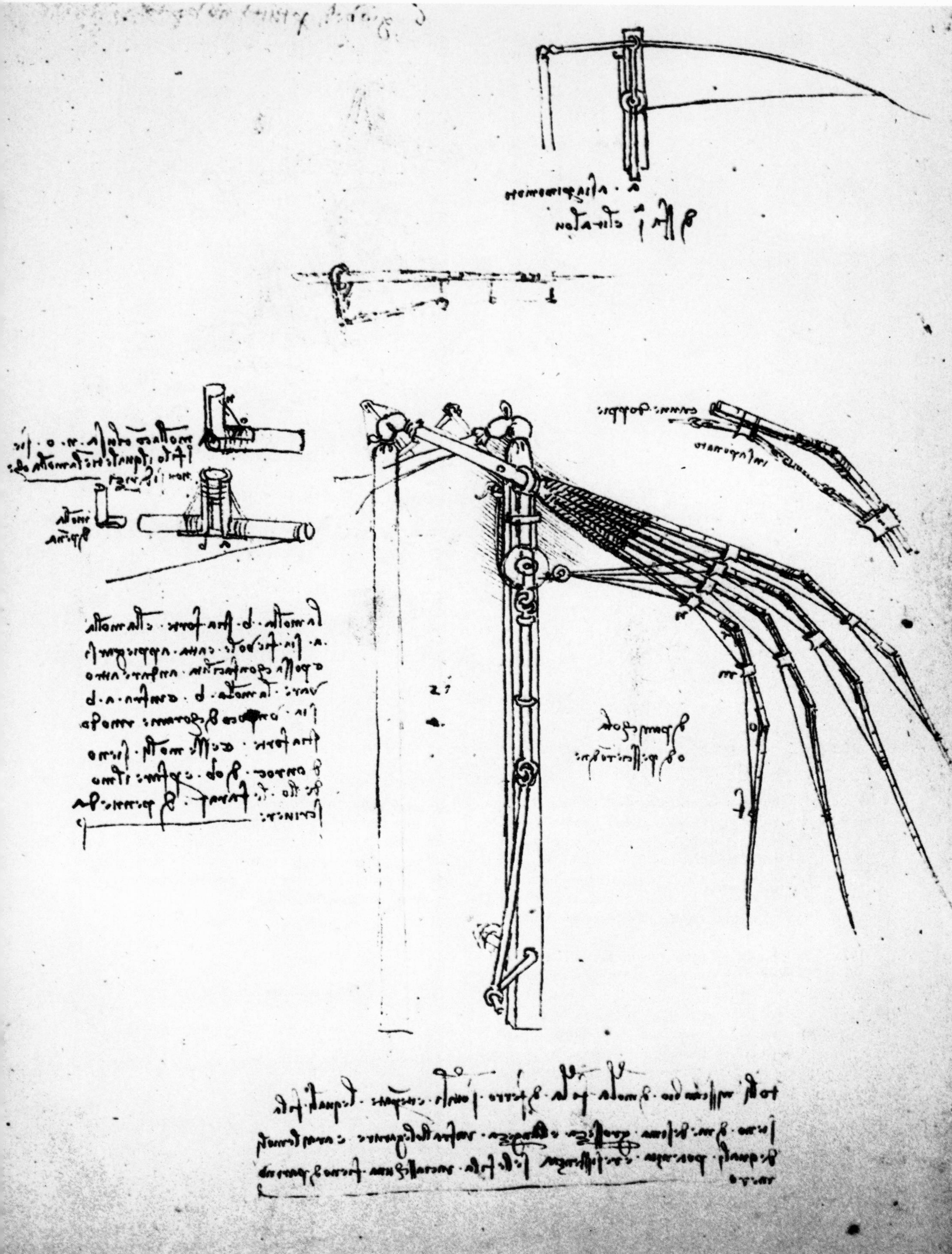

PAGE 140: Study of the Structure of a Wing, c. 1490. Pen and ink. "Dissect the bat," Leonardo wrote, ". . . and on this model arrange the machine. . . . Remember that your bird," as he called his flying machine, "ought not to imitate anything but the bat [because] the bat is aided by the membrane which binds the whole and is impervious." Ambrosiana, Milan

PAGE 141: Study of the Construction of a Flexible Wing, c. 1495. Pen and ink. A framework and the mechanism to work it with a crank, linked shafts, pulleys, and cords. The motion of the joints in the wings was to be regulated by springs of ox horn and thin, tempered steel, which Leonardo describes on the drawing, so that, as the wing moves, its articulated parts also move consistently and automatically. "In constructing wings," he noted, "one should make one cord to bear the strain, and a looser one in the same position to serve the same function." Ambrosiana, Milan

Study of the Construction and Control of a Wing, c. 1490. Pen and ink. The batlike wing was Leonardo's first idea from which, perhaps as the result of a partial recognition that more than a simple rowing motion was necessary, the wing with flexible construction was evolved. Ambrosiana, Milan

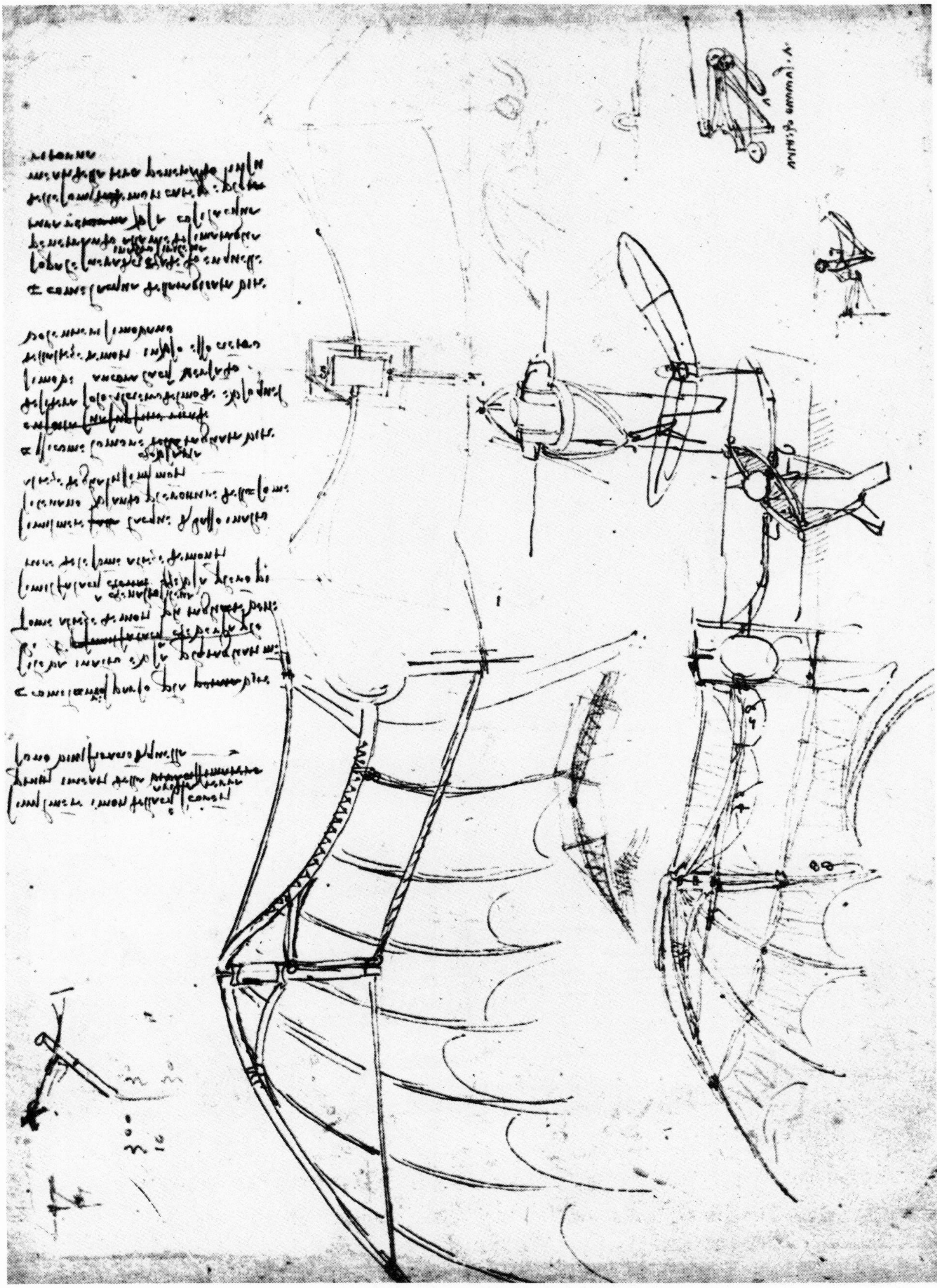

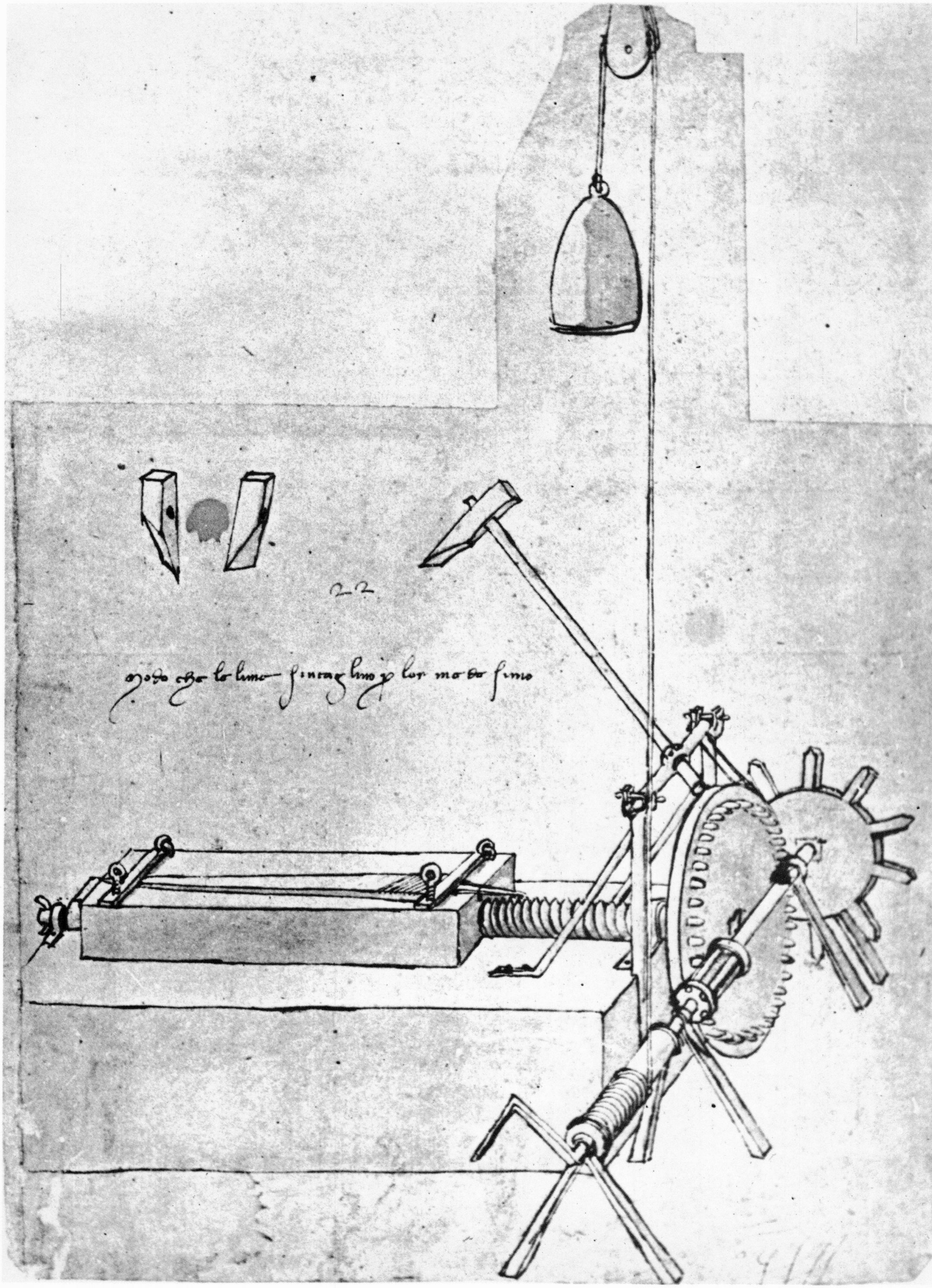
22
modo che le lime sintaglino p lor medesime

"The Paradise of Mathematical Sciences"

Many of the ideas sketched in Leonardo's notebooks are clearly theoretical in character, without implication that he intended that particular form to be realized in a working model. Others are visual notations of machines already in use, or suggestions for mechanical refinements on known devices. To call all of these indiscriminately inventions is to misunderstand the progress of science as well as the unique importance of Leonardo's achievement. The course of scientific development is not only uneven but also cumulative, with each major breakthrough being the result of a series of countless lesser discoveries or insights that make it possible. Often the advance is almost imperceptible; then in times of radical change, as in the Renaissance and again in the nineteenth and twentieth centuries, progress comes at a breathless pace. But always the great individual achievements are made possible by innumerable minor ones: a process has been started and the time is ripe.

As a practicing engineer, Leonardo designed many machines that worked, and invented many things of great significance, such as link chains and various types of gears, the conical screw, and the parachute, to name but a few among many. But his basic improvements on existing machines were just as important and also constitute inventions, though each such machine is the result of many individual and often anonymous contributions, sometimes evolved through the course of centuries. Leonardo's unique achievement was the ability, in mechanics as in anatomy, to think creatively in terms of function. "We see" in his notebooks, as Abbott Payson Usher has pointed out in *The History of Mechanical Inventions,* "many a later invention expressed as pure concept." His imagination encompassed both the solution of problems in a way that was immediately attainable, and ideas so remote that it took centuries for their realization.

Before Leonardo's day there were many treatises on mechanics and engineering, the sources of which almost inevitably go back to ancient times. But all were intended as adjuncts to experience already acquired. As Bertrand Gille, historian of the National Archives in Paris, has written, "Technical processes were not taught in schools, they were learned in practice." In them, machines that perform various tasks are described. There are watermills, windmills, looms, clocks, and innumerable others, but each is treated as if it were an isolated thing, unique in itself, without continuity from one to another, even when the same principle is employed. Leonardo's contribution was to analyze the basic question and interpret it by means of the underlying principle and thus define problems in

---

File-making Machine, c. 1490. Pen and ink and wash. This machine embodies two ideas of importance: the use of a threaded shaft to control automatically the movement of the file blank so that it may be evenly scored by the hammer, and the use of a falling weight as a power source, a clockwork device here given industrial application. Thus the machine represents a step toward Leonardo's ideal of automation. Ambrosiana, Milan

terms which made their eventual solution achievable. He was also the first to conceive of mechanics, really applied science, as a matter of power source, power transmission, and power utilization so organized as to demand as little human supervision and control as possible.

"Mechanics," Leonardo wrote, "is the paradise of mathematical sciences because here we come to the fruit of mathematics." For him mathematics provided a "supreme certainty," a means of analysis and of understanding. He based his studies of flight on the proposition that "a bird is an instrument working according to mathematical law" and thus the principles of flight were capable of being understood by man. It was central to an understanding of life also, because for him "instrumental or mechanical science is the noblest and above all others the most useful, seeing that by means of it all animated bodies which have movement perform all their actions."

He had an amazing intuition, far in advance of his time, of ideas basic to physical science, such as the concept of inertia, the tendency of any object to continue in a given state, whether of motion or stability; of force, and of gravity. "A weight which has no support," he wrote, "falls by the shortest route to the lowest point, which is the center of the world." Such theoretical concepts, two centuries before Newton, as well as his extreme practicality are combined in the many observations and devices which fill his notebooks. Preoccupied with accuracy, he urged that an "experiment should be made many times so that no accident may occur to hinder or falsify the proof," and advised all to "shun the precepts of those whose arguments are not confirmed by experience."

Another of the dreams of ages was the achievement of perpetual motion. It is no wonder, therefore, that Leonardo studied the practicability of the idea, and even went as far as to design a device to test his theory that the notion was impossible. It is typical that it involves the use of water as a source of power, because he was constantly preoccupied with water, its flow and action, its force and beauty. He fitted a waterwheel into a trough and fastened scoops to the wheel so that, as it turned from the action of the water flowing against its fins, it would also scoop up water to the higher level of the trough in order to continue providing motive power for the wheel. Needless to say, this device, like several others he tried, was unsuccessful. Satisfied by his results, he dismissed the "speculators on perpetual motion" as "companions of the searchers for gold," for alchemy, the pseudoscience which claimed to turn base metals into gold, was another of the persistent dreams of men from early times, and Leonardo regarded it, too, as folly.

We can be pretty sure that he knew why perpetual motion is impossible because he also carried on many experiments with the problems of friction, devising roller bearings, which he tested by applying them to the wheels of a cart with a rotating axle. He was delighted to discover what modern science has proved, that they are, like the ball bearings which he also tested, highly satisfactory as "friction removers." He tried out lubricants, such as soap and grease, to see their effect on the effort required to move heavy bodies on planes of different slopes. He experimented with pulleys, levers, and with the screw, which he recognized as a spiral form of the inclined plane, and consequently to be studied in similar terms.

The form of the spiral, of which the screw is an application, occurs often in nature and interested Leonardo. He designed lifting devices using the principle of the screw, one of which seems to have been intended for use in the handling of heavy cannon. To make the threaded rod needed for such machines, he designed a screw cutter that would make the spiral channel-

Screw-cutting Machine. Pen and ink. The principle of the screw was first applied in ancient times as a fastener for bracelets, then gradually came into broader use: to raise weights with the jack, to bore holes with the augur, to apply pressure as in an olive press or vise, to produce motion as with the propeller of a ship, and to raise water with the screw of Archimedes. Leonardo's screw-cutting machine was to produce threaded shafts for such uses as in the file cutter and the printing press. A reproduction of it has worked successfully. Institut de France, Paris ➤

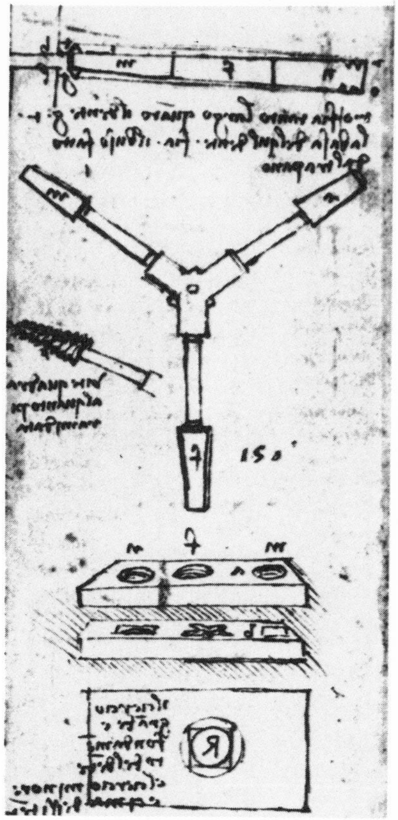

ings in a straight, dowel-like shaft of wood or of iron. Then he designed a tool for threading a hole to receive such a rod, as in a nut. A threaded rod also provides an excellent way of producing controlled and even motion, as in the file-making machine.

These machines were not to be substantially improved until 1830 when Henry Maudslay, the English inventor, using the same principle of control by the threaded rod, perfected the modern lathe, planer, and milling machine, with a supremely accurate slide-rest, "a mechanical contrivance in place of the human hand." Directly following Leonardo's system, lengths of threaded rod reproduced themselves in Maudslay's screw-cutting lathes because the threaded rods already made governed and controlled the pitch and depth of the cutting of the new thread in the new rod.

Water pipes were made from ancient times out of bored logs fitted end to end, and Leo-

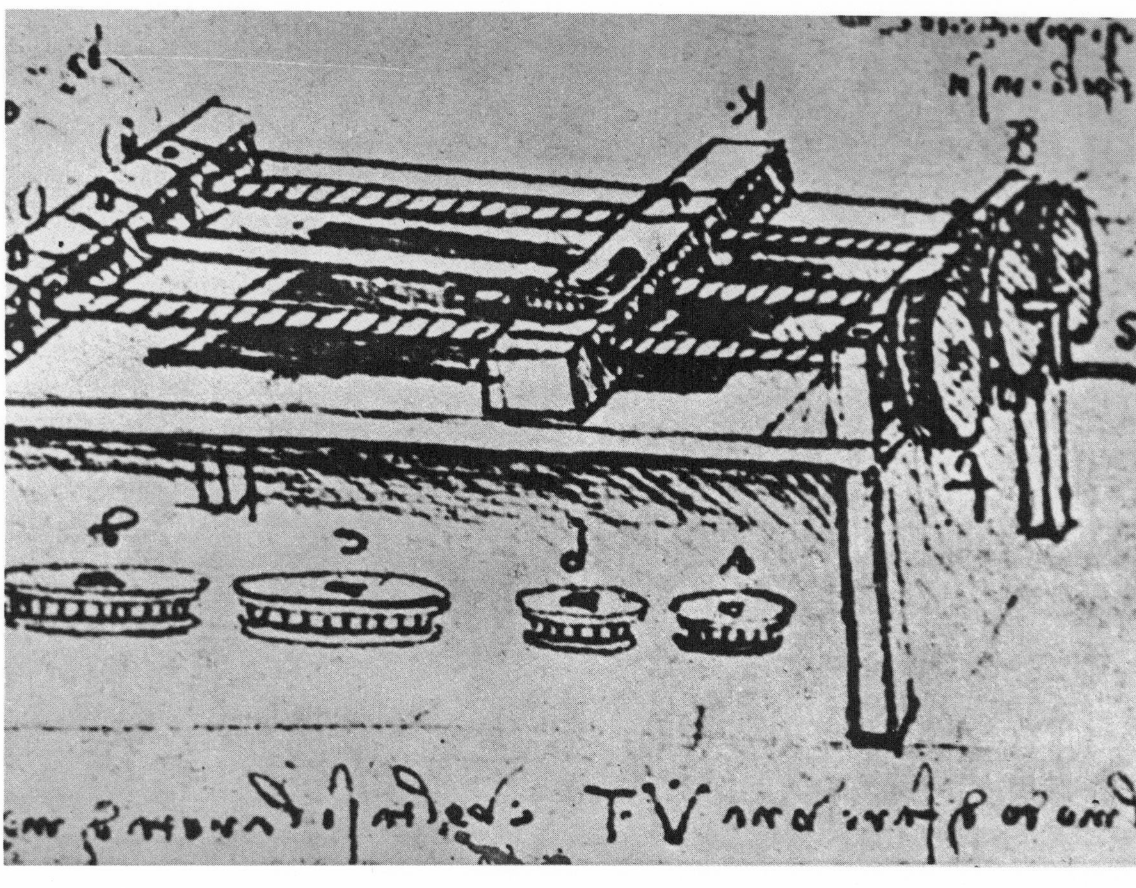

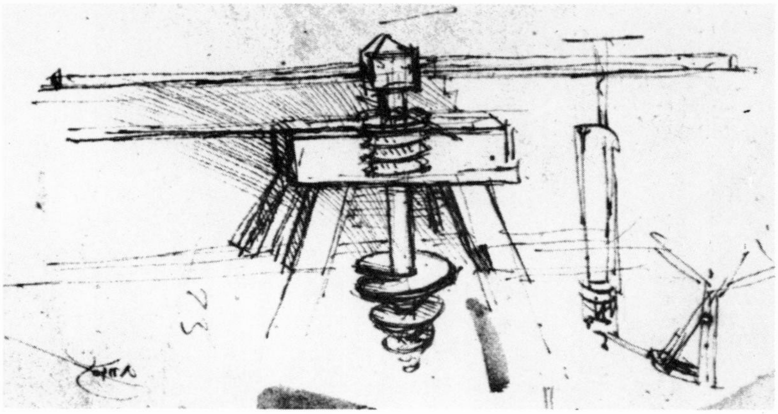

"A borer to drill into the ground to find water."

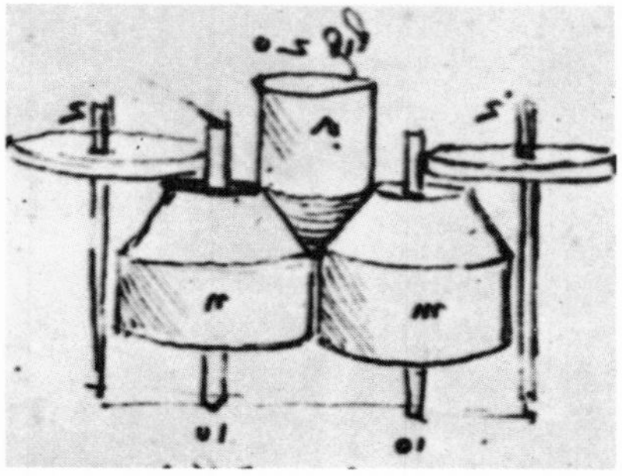

nardo sketched a machine for boring logs vertically, so that the chips from the operation would fall out of the hole and keep it clear for the borer. To accomplish this, the machine used a threaded rod gradually to raise the boring mechanism as it pierced the log. He made drawings of well-drilling machines and other earth borers, either for postholes or perhaps to penetrate an enemy's mining operation during a siege. Another military application of the threaded rod and the borer is an apparatus to enable a diver to make an underwater hole in an enemy ship.

He was aware of the advantages of the screw as a fastener, much as it is used today in all sorts of ways, from putting up shelves in the kitchen to the assembly of automobiles, so he used the conical screw as well, and made a drawing of a polisher for bronze screws which were perhaps first cast, then cleaned and sharpened with the polisher. Such metal screws came into general use in the sixteenth century.

Just as he tried to eliminate or diminish friction with lubricants and bearings, he also experimented with the positive use of friction in a system to transmit power from one roller to others with which it is engaged in an application of the principle of the modern friction clutch. He used friction in other positive ways, such as in machines for the grinding of lenses and the polishing of mirrors, both of which show ingenious uses of eccentric mountings to produce regular and controlled abrasive action. He was interested in the transformation of one sort of motion into another because of this practicality of application, and made drawings of several devices to change circular motion into elliptical, and oscillatory (back and forth) action into continuous rotary motion.

His favorite type of transmission, however, was the form used by Vitruvius and devised in the ancient world, the cog and lantern wheels. He knew and used, however, the toothed gears so widely employed today, including spiral gears, with the teeth at an angle, which he recognized as more durable because the bearing surfaces are larger. Both appear in drawings dealing with transmission devices. In one of them, three cogged wheels of varying diameters are engaged with the single, conical lantern wheel to demonstrate the principle used in the transmission of the modern automobile.

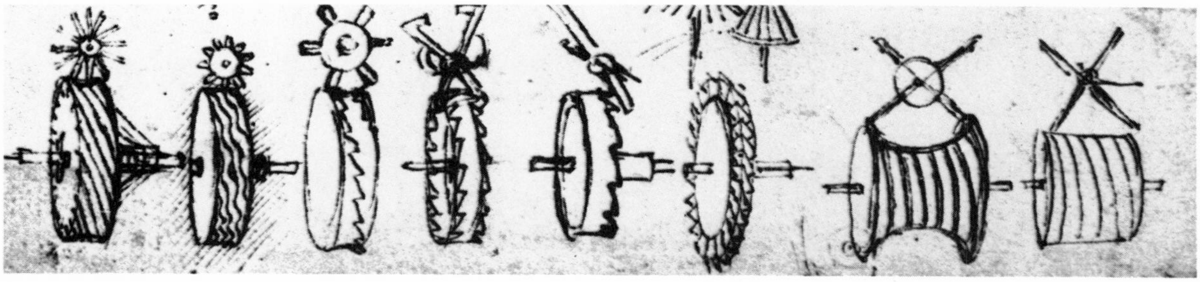

He applied these ideas to such practical uses as a turnspit built into a fireplace with the power supplied by a fan mounted on a shaft high in the chimney. The spit was turned by the hot air rising from the fire roasting the meat below; another spit was turned by a weight on a cord which works by being wound up like a grandfather's clock. Such a use of weights as a driving mechanism dates from far back into the pre-Christian era, while the use of gears, though ancient, is of somewhat more recent origin.

Many of the ideas expressed in drawings and diagrams obviously have to do with problems that arose in connection with various projects on which he was working as an engineer. Construction constantly requires the lifting and handling of heavy weights, so sketches for weight-lifting devices recur throughout his notebooks. He had ideas for making use of screws, pulleys, levers, and even the expansive force of steam and the explosion of gunpowder to drive upward a piston in a cylinder as in the modern internal combustion engine.

Milan was one of the centers of the cloth industry, so he designed silk-reeling and -twisting machinery and an almost complete set of machines for the production of woolens: a spinning machine, a power loom, a gig mill for raising the nap of the cloth, and a shearing machine. The spinning and nap-raising machines are sound in principle, and have features in common with mechanisms then in use as well as others later to be developed. The sketches for the loom are fragmentary and it is hard to tell whether they are a record of the form in which they were used at that time or his original interpretations. His flyer, with its level-winding motion, has been called his "most complete and original achievement . . . in this field," and looks directly forward to the form developed during the eighteenth century by the Englishmen Lewis Paul and Sir Richard Arkwright, which is virtually the type in use today. His shearing engine, however, is purely theoretical, being based on the double-bladed principle of handshears rather than that of rotating blades, as in the lawnmower, which proved to be the successful solution.

Because Milan was also a city of metalworkers, his notebooks contain schemes for a mill for rolling metal into sheets and for drawing it into bars for the construction of cannon, though he felt that the waterpower he first proposed for the latter operation would not make it fast enough for practicality. Both these ideas were to wait a considerable length of time before they were fully developed.

The lathe has been known since very early times, and Leonardo's drawing of one depicts a common type. He devised another closely related machine set up for a horizontal boring operation. Though not sufficiently detailed for complete clarity, it shows his knowledge of all the improvements of the machines of the latest type to date. His olive-oil press is a somewhat more advanced version of a type which had been in general use from Classic times.

His work on the printing press shows that he was aware of the potential evolution of which it proved capable. The early presses, such as those used by Gutenberg, were ponderous and slow affairs, needing the attention of several men. Leonardo attempted mechanically to relate the printing frame, which holds the type, and the screw, which exerts the pressure necessary for printing, thus increasing the automation and making for greater ease, speed, and control. The first real improvements in the press had to await the early seventeenth century, however, to begin its slow evolution toward the modern high-speed rotary presses which today flood the world with constant streams of printed matter. Leonardo's consciousness of the significance of these things is shown by the note which accompanies his drawings of the power loom. "This is second only to the printing press in importance; no less useful in its practical application; a lucrative, beautiful, and subtle invention."

Before 1250 there were only sundials and water clocks by which to tell the time. The first mechanical clocks were immense awkward affairs, sometimes weighing tons, with iron wheels, which were made by a blacksmith. The first known example is that installed in the tower of the chapel of the Castle of Milan in 1335. It struck each of the twenty-four hours of the day according to the Italian fashion, "which is of the greatest use to men of every degree," a contemporary observer noted. It was still functioning when Leonardo was there, so he may have examined its ponderous mechanism as well as regulated his days by its bell. Such clocks, however, were inclined to be inaccurate, and had to be corrected by reference to sundials.

By the fifteenth century clockmaking was much advanced, and Leonardo designed a clock in which he separated the train of gears telling the hours from that telling the minutes, each being driven by a separate weight to gain greater accuracy. It had been common to separate the going, or time-telling, train from the striking, or hour-ringing train, but not to separate the hours from the minutes in this way. All the early clocks had but a single hand to tell the hour, and it is generally accepted that the first clocks to tell minutes were those made in Germany in the fifteenth century. Such more advanced clocks actually served as chronometers for the early astronomers, though Tycho Brahe, the famous Danish scientist of the second half of the sixteenth century, still checked his time by direct astronomical observation for the sake of accuracy.

To regulate the speed, which would be totally out of control without some such device, Leonardo used a variation of what is called the verge balance, introduced a century or more earlier, which alternately engaged and released two toothed gears, thus giving the mechanism the characteristic rhythmic, ticking movement later commonly achieved through the use of the

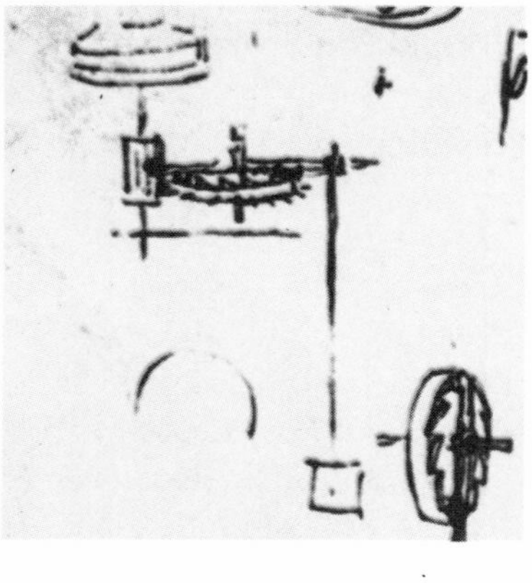

pendulum. Leonardo understood the use of the pendulum to regulate movement because drawings of it in a form applicable to clocks appear in his notebooks. Whether he actually intended so to apply it is unclear, but if so, he anticipated its introduction into common usage for this purpose by at least a century and a half.

Leonardo was concerned with accurate measurement not only of time, as in his dual-train clock, but also of heights and distances, both important for making maps and laying out canals. He designed an apparatus for estimating the heights of mountains, another to show the degree of incline of a surface, and, to measure distance, he borrowed a wheelbarrowlike device, called an hodometer, from Vitruvius. It

had a system of gears so arranged that at every mile traveled by the carefully calculated circumference of the wheel, a small round stone dropped into a chamber. At the end of the distance to be measured one had merely to count the stones. Not satisfied with this, Leonardo replaced the stone-dropping mechanism with a dial, so that not only miles but fractions of miles could be noted. He designed a pedometer to register the number of steps taken over a certain distance by means of a pendulum that swung once at each step, its motion reduced through a train of three gears to record the number on a dial. When used by an experienced person who has learned to regulate his stride such an instrument can be accurate enough to be useful.

He also designed an alarm clock of a truly alarming character. It employed the principle of the water clock, being actuated by the steady, tiny trickle of water from one container to another. By properly regulating the amount of water poured into the container, at a certain point the balance of the weight of the water is reversed, setting off a lever which "jerks violently upward the feet of the sleeper, who is thus awakened and goes about his business," probably in much the same state of shocked nerves as if the water itself had been suddenly poured over him.

The use of a falling weight as a source of power came to be so completely associated with clocks that it has been considered a purely clockwork mechanism from the later Middle Ages on. But Leonardo, as we have seen, applied it to all sorts of other devices, including his file cutter, in which the aim of automation is clear, since the mechanism was designed to complete each file without the need of an operator. Though there is no record that such a machine was ever constructed, its principle is sound and workable, and a single person could keep a dozen or more machines in constant production.

He also experimented with another source of power closely associated with clocks since the sixteenth century, the spring. He conjectured using springs to drive a curious self-propelled vehicle he designed, and they also appear as an assistance to manpower in a drawing for one of his many schemes for a flying machine.

The idea embodied in his file cutter, of economy of manpower and standardization of the process, and consequently of the product, was not realized until centuries after Leonardo's day, but his notes and sketches are full of it. His nap-raising machine, for example, could handle five widths of material at once, and his shearing machine four, while his needle grinder was to finish 400 needles in an hour. In his drawings for the various machines to produce coinage for the papal mint, he devised automatic hammers working off a central power source so that eight machines could be in simultaneous controlled production of the metal bars from which coin blanks were stamped. His milling machine was planned to bridge a canalized river with several undershot wheels driving a multiple-unit mill on both sides of the stream. Here, as in so many other of his schemes, the far-reaching implications are of infinitely greater importance than the immediate application, for Leonardo, intensely practical though he was, has an even more significant place as a pioneer in new conceptions than as an inventor of individual devices.

When machines were made individually, each for a separate job, there could be no hope for the standardization necessary to realize Leonardo's revolutionary ideal. It was not until the eighteenth century that mass production was finally achieved through the use of interchangeable parts: in 1765 a French artillery general named Gribeauval produced a number of gun carriages in this way. And in 1784 Thomas Jefferson reported from Paris that he had seen musket locks similarly made. It remained for a Connecticut Yankee named Eli Whitney, the inventor of the cotton gin, to develop the method, considered impossible by leading European military experts, in his production of rifles for the United States government. Another Connecticut man, Eli Terry, applied the same idea to the manufacture of clocks. Sewing machines and agricultural equipment followed. The machine-tool industry was in full swing. And the machine-centered modern world, with its ever-increasing production, was born, and developing automation, as Leonardo had envisioned, began freeing man from the burden of the centuries, slavery to manual labor, with results so revolutionary that we have not yet been able to understand or control them.

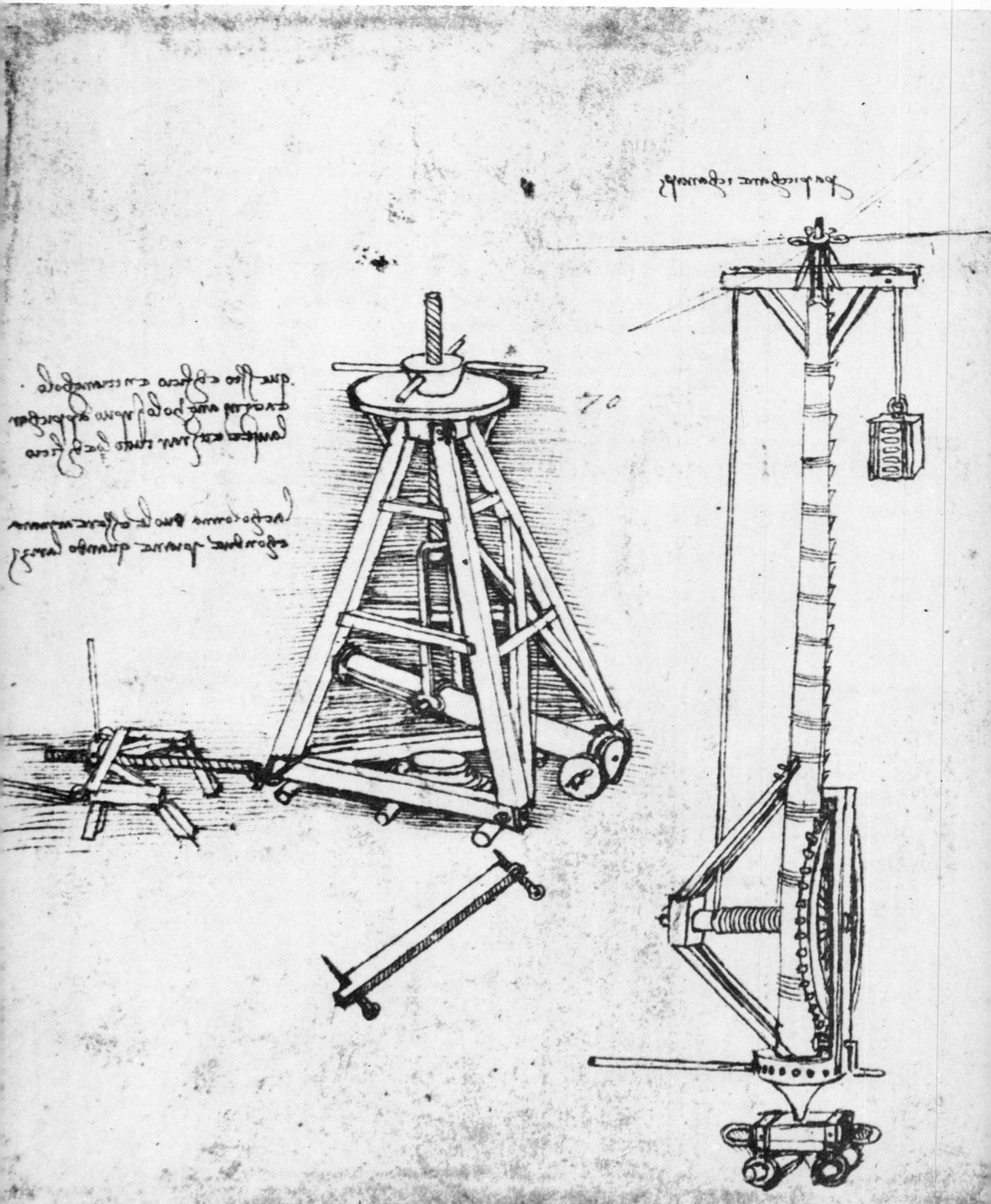

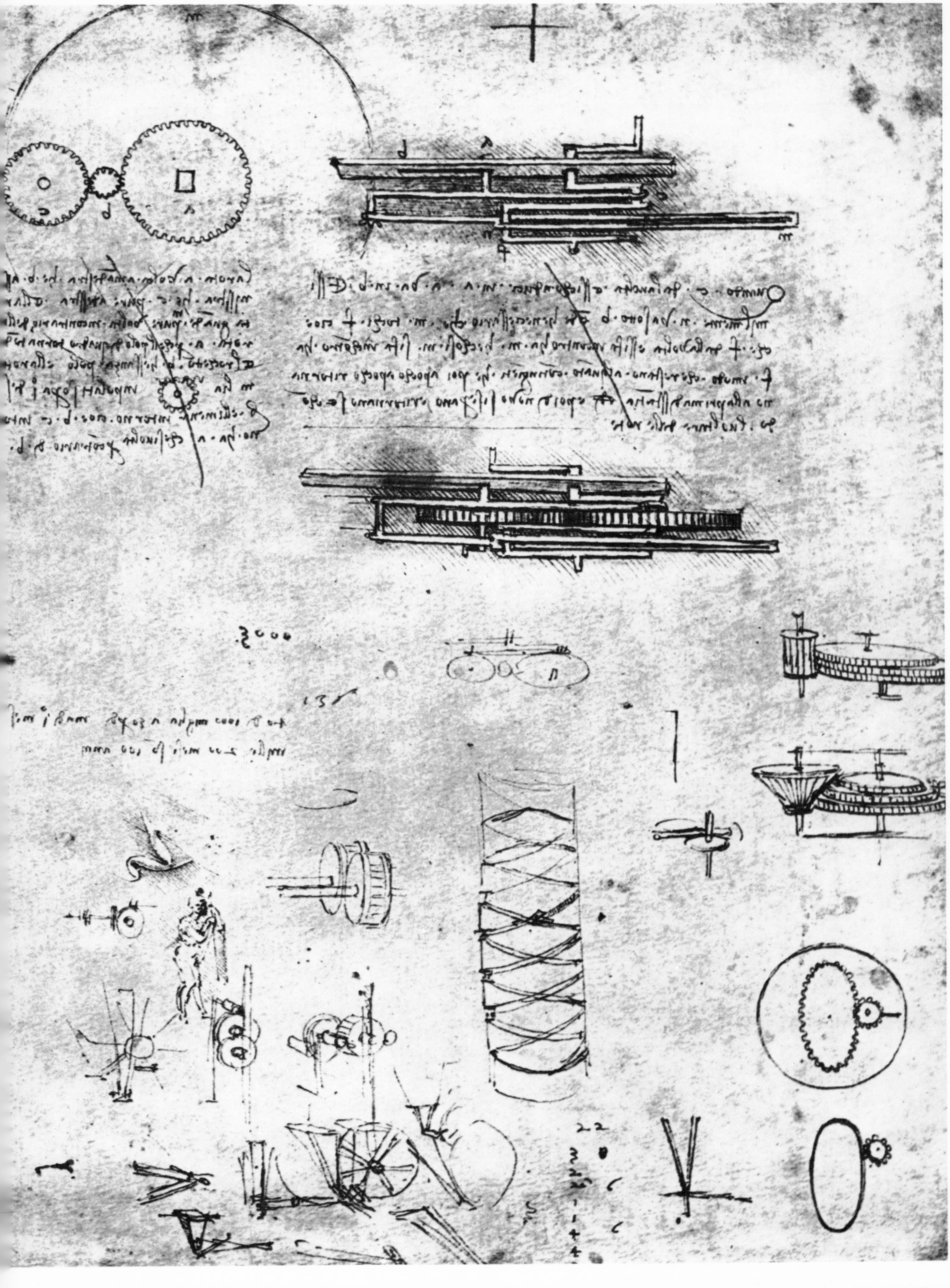

PAGE 152: Two Lifting Devices. Pen and ink. The one to the left is mounted on shear legs for raising cannon with a screw, and is moved on rollers with a winch. That to the right, mounted on a wheeled truck and guided by an overhead wire is worked with a windlass and pulleys. Ambrosiana, Milan

PAGE 153: Studies of Gear Systems and Transmission Devices. Pen and ink. Leonardo's interest in the transmission of motive force and the transformation of one sort of movement into another appears here in several sketches. Above are three gear systems, that to the left resembling modern clockwork, while the two in side view employ the principle of the crank. To the right are two three-speed systems which employ his favorite cog and lantern wheels, and work according to the principle of the transmission of the modern automobile. Ambrosiana, Milan

Sketch of a Printing Press, c. 1485–90. Pen and ink. In his design for a printing press, Leonardo related the action of the press and the printing frame through the screw and cogged wheel and lantern pinion in order to further automate the process. It was many years before anything approaching this degree of refinement took place in printing-press construction. Ambrosiana, Milan

Two Types of Turnspit. Pen and ink. Devices such as this were known since ancient times. That above uses the clockwork mechanism of the falling weight, with a fan vaned with goose feathers as a governor. That below shows Leonardo's knowledge of the principle of convection, since the spit is turned through the action of the rising hot air on the fan set in the chimney flue. Ambrosiana, Milan

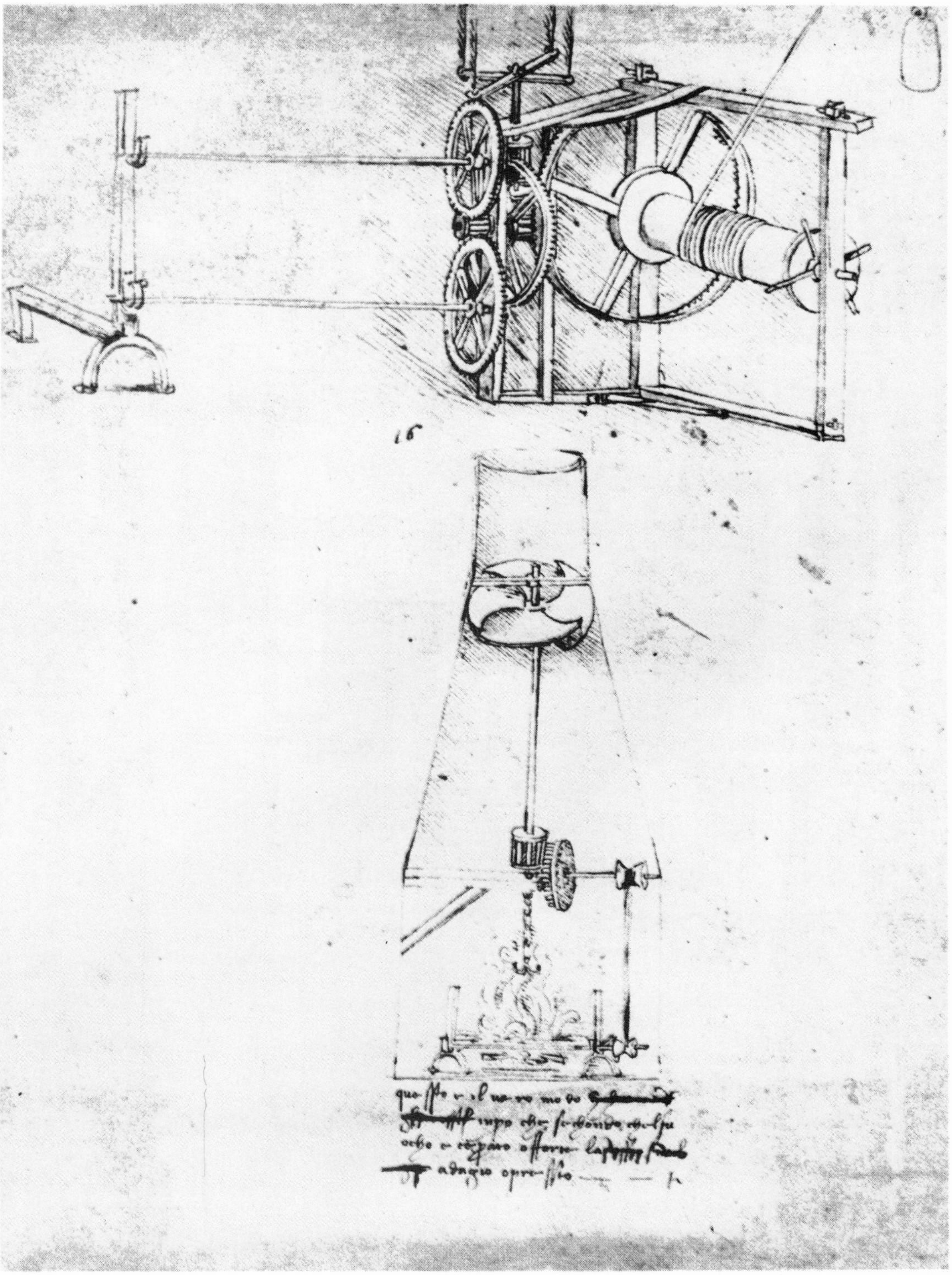
16
questo è il vero modo
… che secondo che 'l fu-
oco è temperato o forte la …
adagio o presto

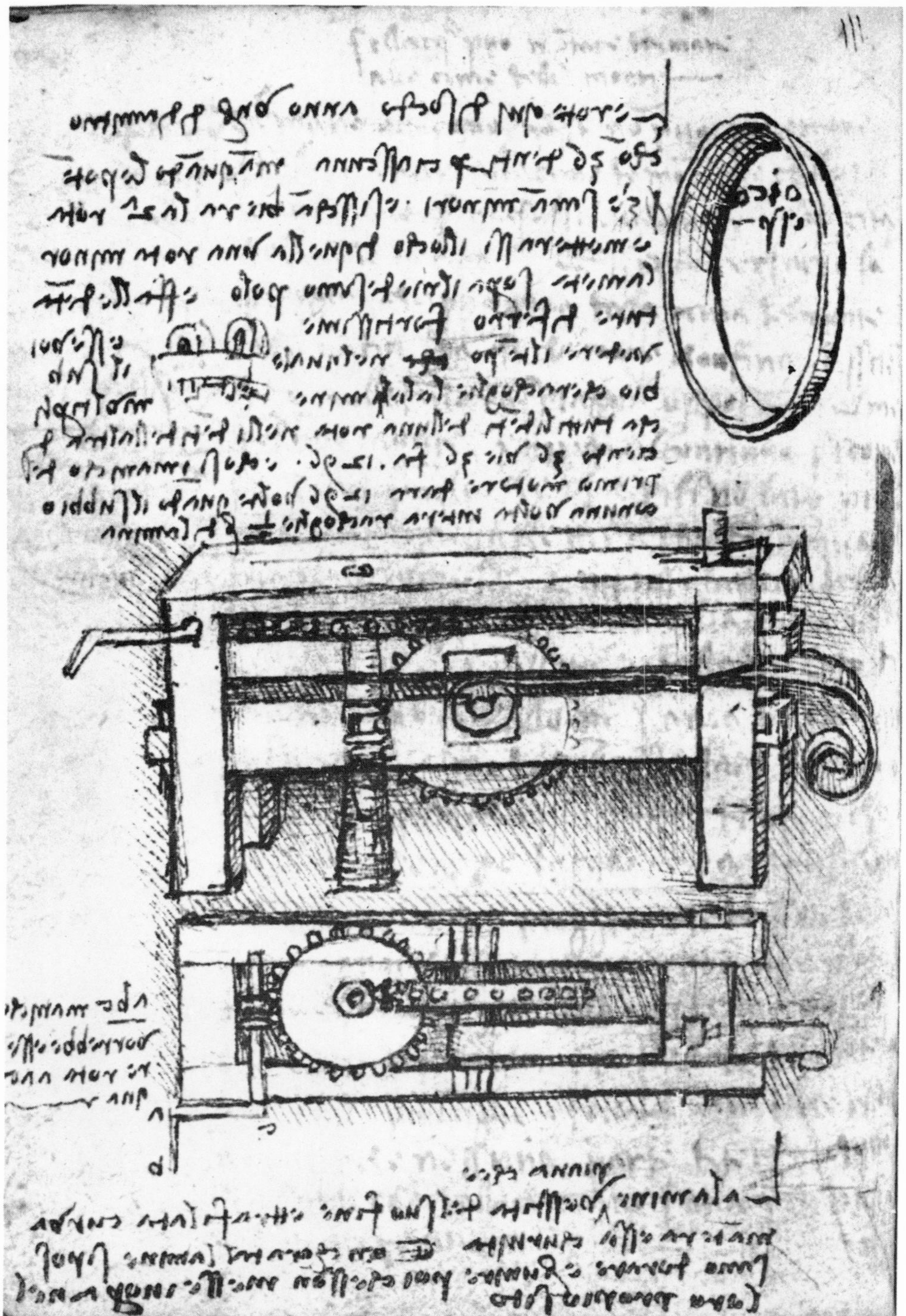

Machine for Drawing Thin Strips of Metal, c. 1485–90. Pen and ink. Designed to produce sheets of copper suitable for making mirrors, the machine is drawn both in plan and elevation, rarely found among Leonardo's sketches. He designed similar machines for rolling sheet tin, sheet lead for roofing, and sheet gold. Institut de France, Paris

Machine for Drawing Iron Bars, c. 1485–95. Pen and ink. Designed to produce iron staves for the construction of cannon, this machine was to be powered by water, though Leonardo doubted the action would be fast enough. The form of the waterwheel suggests the cased wheel or hydraulic turbine that Leonardo devised as a more efficient power source than either an undershot wheel run by the pressure of the flow of the stream, or an overshot wheel run by the weight of the falling water. Ambrosiana, Milan

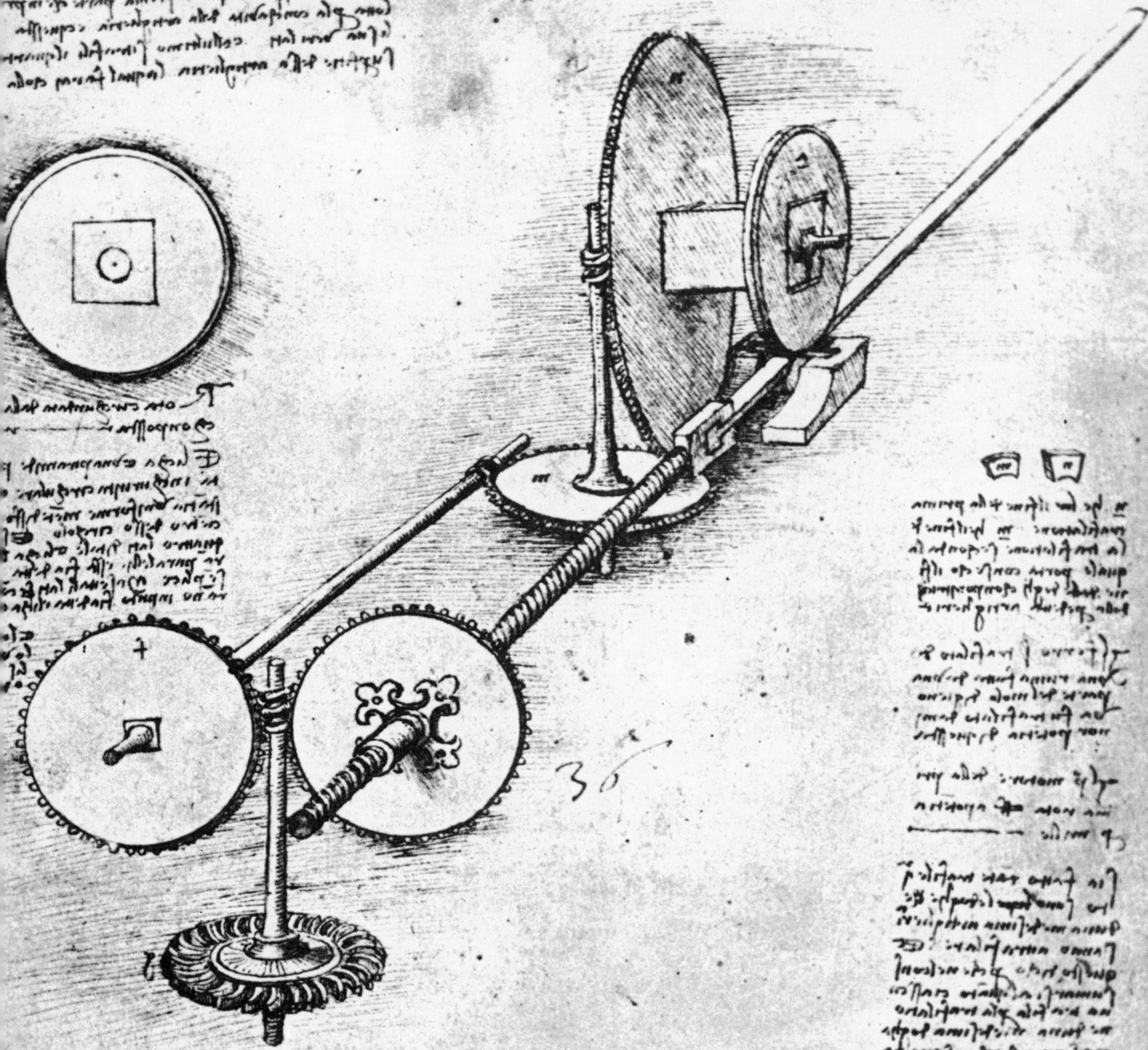

36

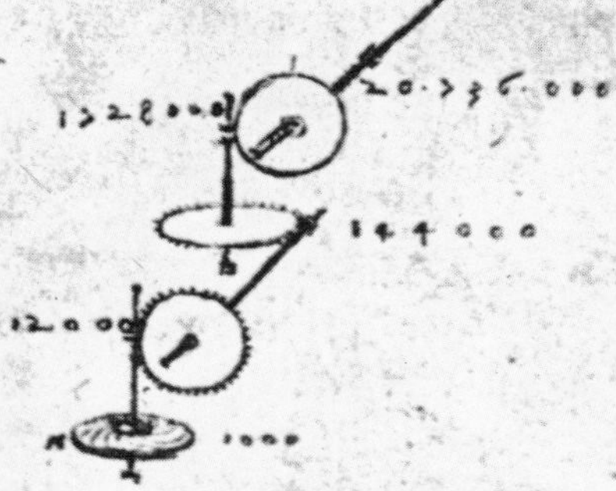

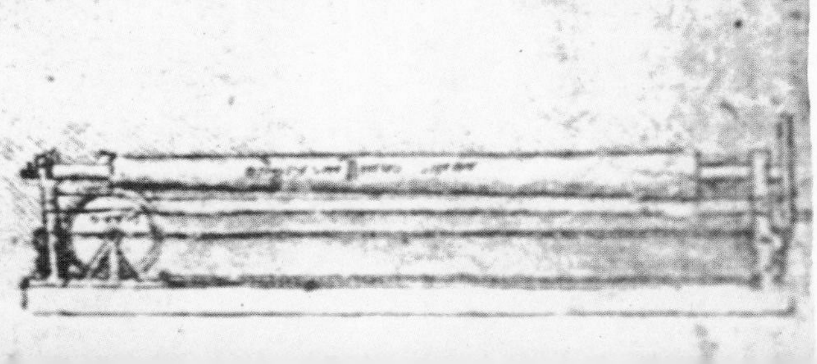

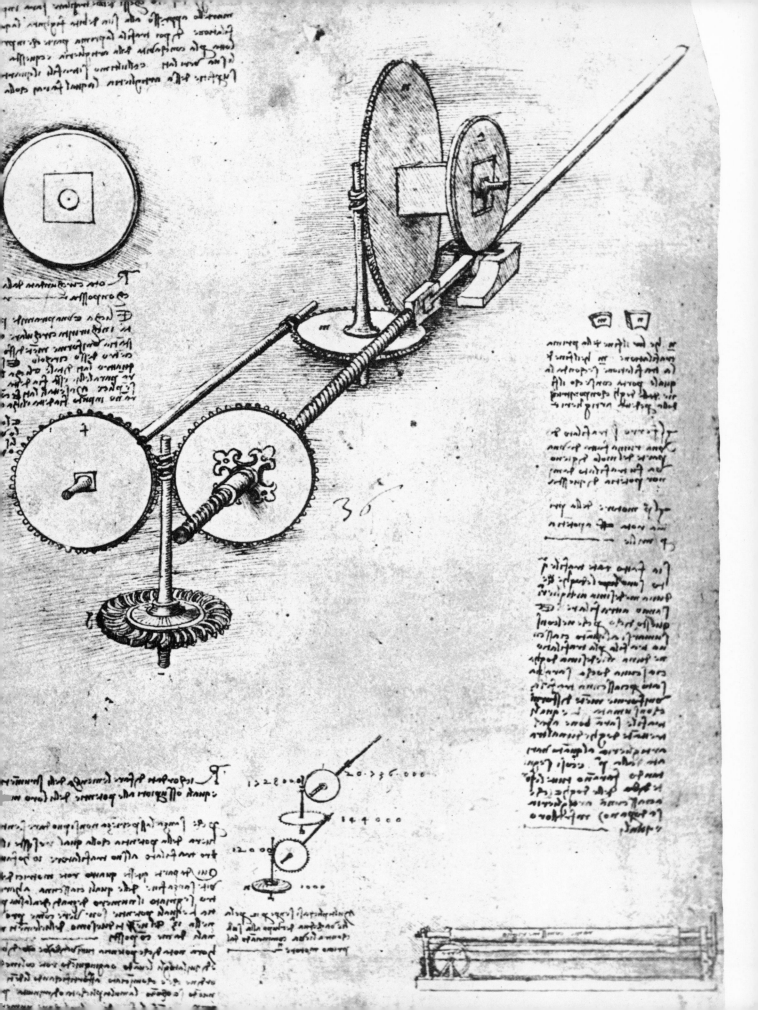

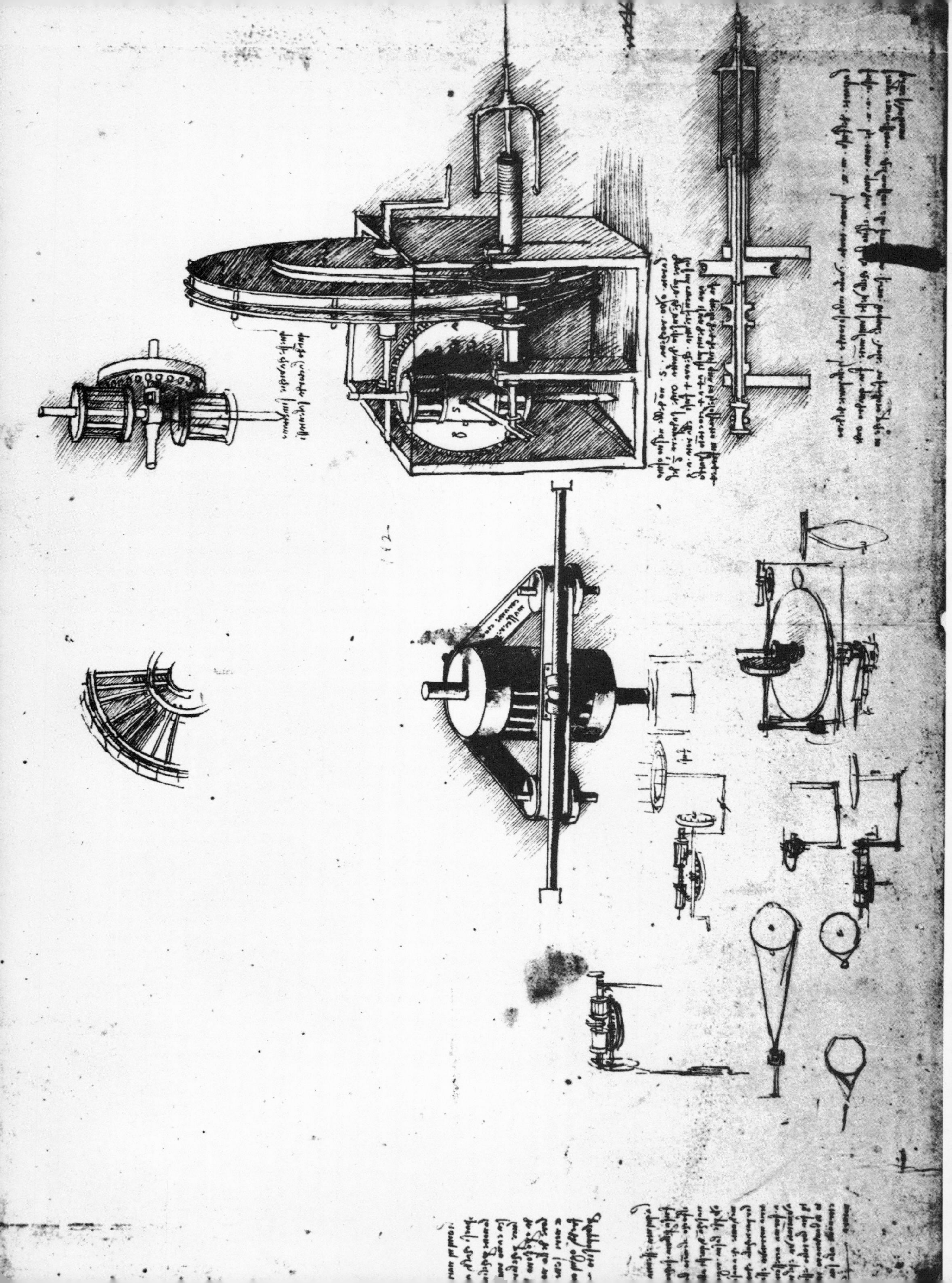

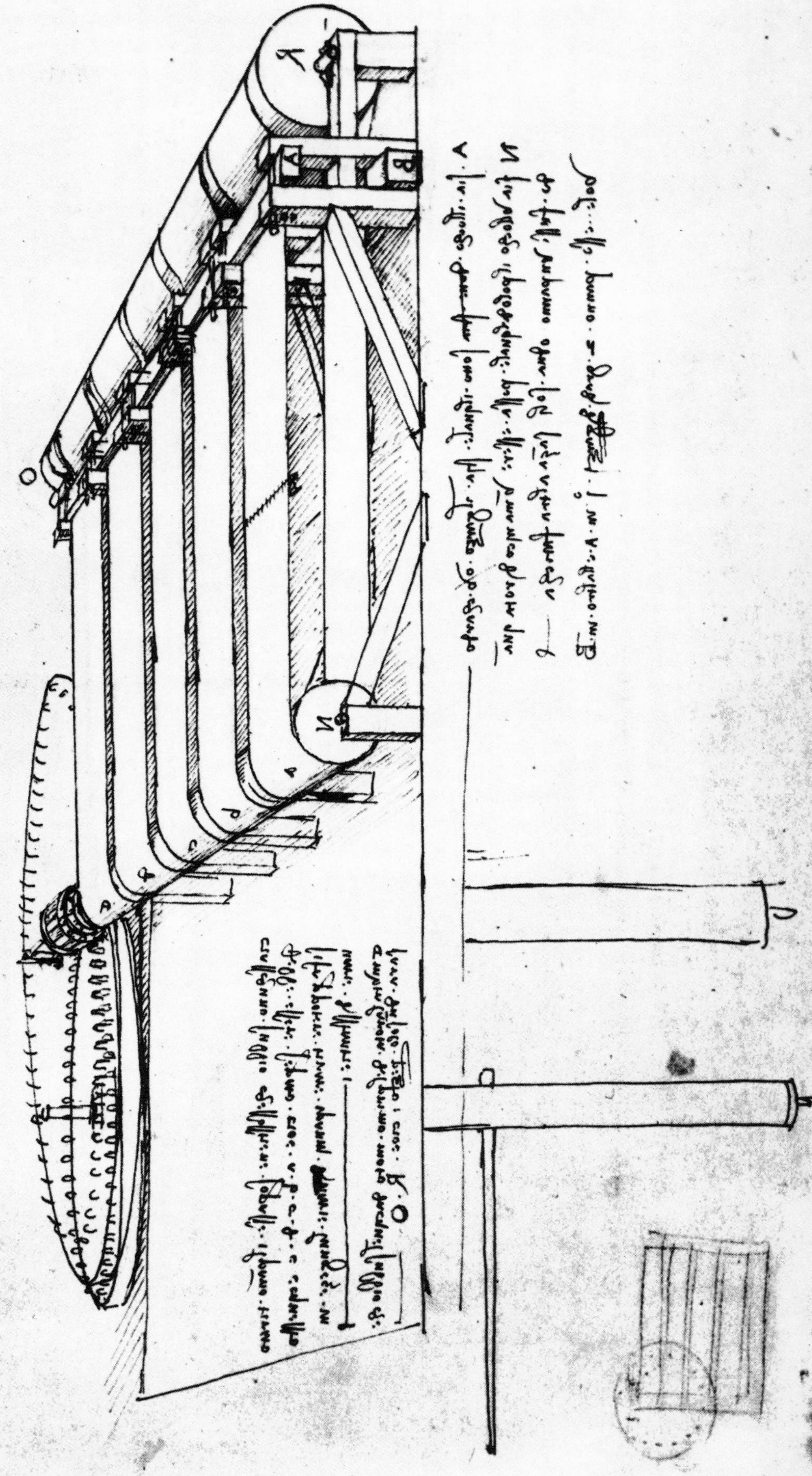

PAGE 158: Spinning Machine with Flyer, c. 1485. Pen and ink. Because Milan was a textile center, Leonardo designed a series of textile machines, including those for spinning, weaving, shearing, and nap raising. In his spinning machine, with its flyer and level-winding action, he anticipated by more than two centuries the work of two eighteenth-century Englishmen, Paul and Arkwright, whose machines were the start of modern production. Ambrosiana, Milan

PAGE 159: Nap-raising Machine, c. 1485. Pen and ink. Probably powered by a horse or donkey working the winch below, this machine was designed to handle five widths of material at once. Ambrosiana, Milan

Studies of a Lathe, Olive-oil Press, and Worm Gearing, c. 1485–95. Pen and ink. To cut the threaded shafts shown at lower left, Leonardo sketched the turning lathe above, worked with a treadle using the reciprocal action of the bow. The olive-oil press is a version of a type in use since Classic times. A horse or donkey, hitched to the curved end of the arm, counter-weighted to keep it level, was driven around the press to supply power to screw the press down to press out the juice. Ambrosiana, Milan

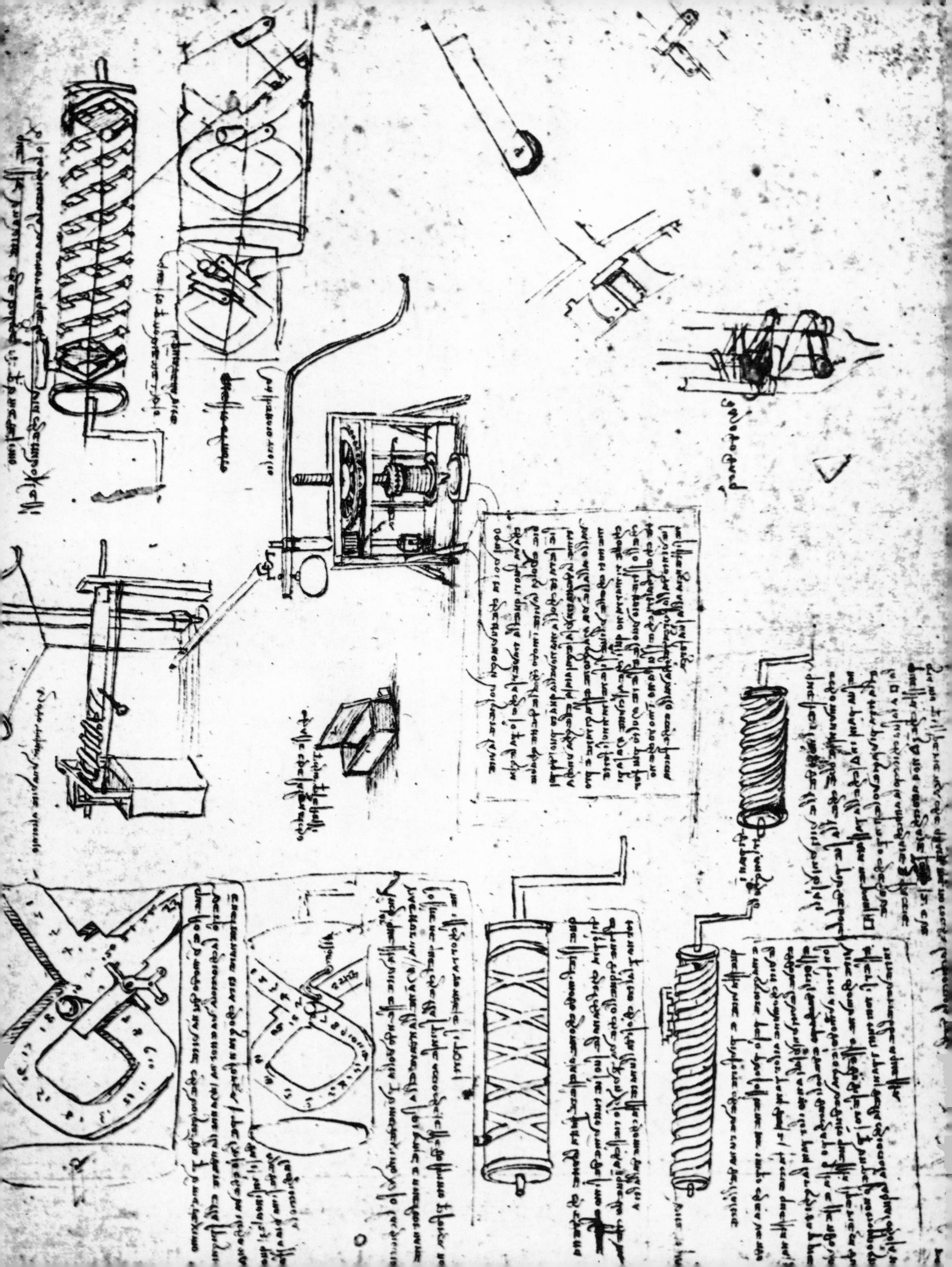

An Earth-moving Machine, c. 1485. Pen and ink and wash. Because of his responsibilities for the canals of Lombardy, Leonardo was constantly working on improvements of existing methods and equipment and devising new ones. This canal-digging machine with twin cranes is an ancestor of modern earth-moving machinery used in road building, site preparation, and surface mining. Ambrosiana, Milan

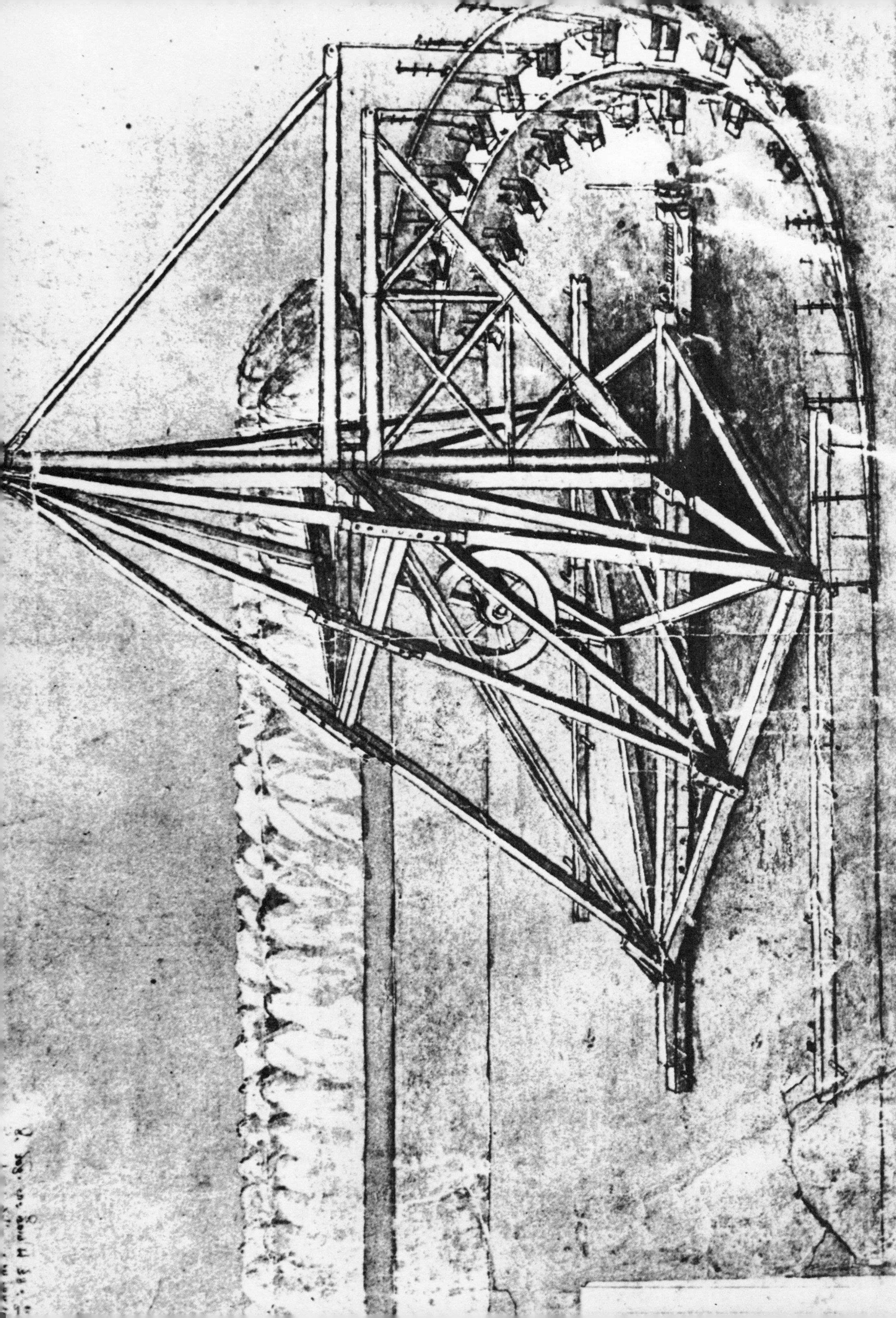

Automatic Hammer, 1515–16. Pen and ink. When Leonardo was in Rome during these years he designed a series of machines for the papal mint. Among them were a draw bench to ensure uniformity of the strips of metal by drawing them through dies, stamps to cut the blanks out of the strips "quite as round as sieves made for sorting chestnuts," dies to impress the design on the blanks, and the automatic hammer, apparently intended to be one of eight working off the same vertical shaft, showing Leonardo's ideal of automatic production. The improvements that Benvenuto Cellini, famous as a goldsmith, later initiated in the papal mint (and also in the mint of Henry II in France) were based in large measure on ideas earlier conceived by Leonardo. Ambrosiana, Milan

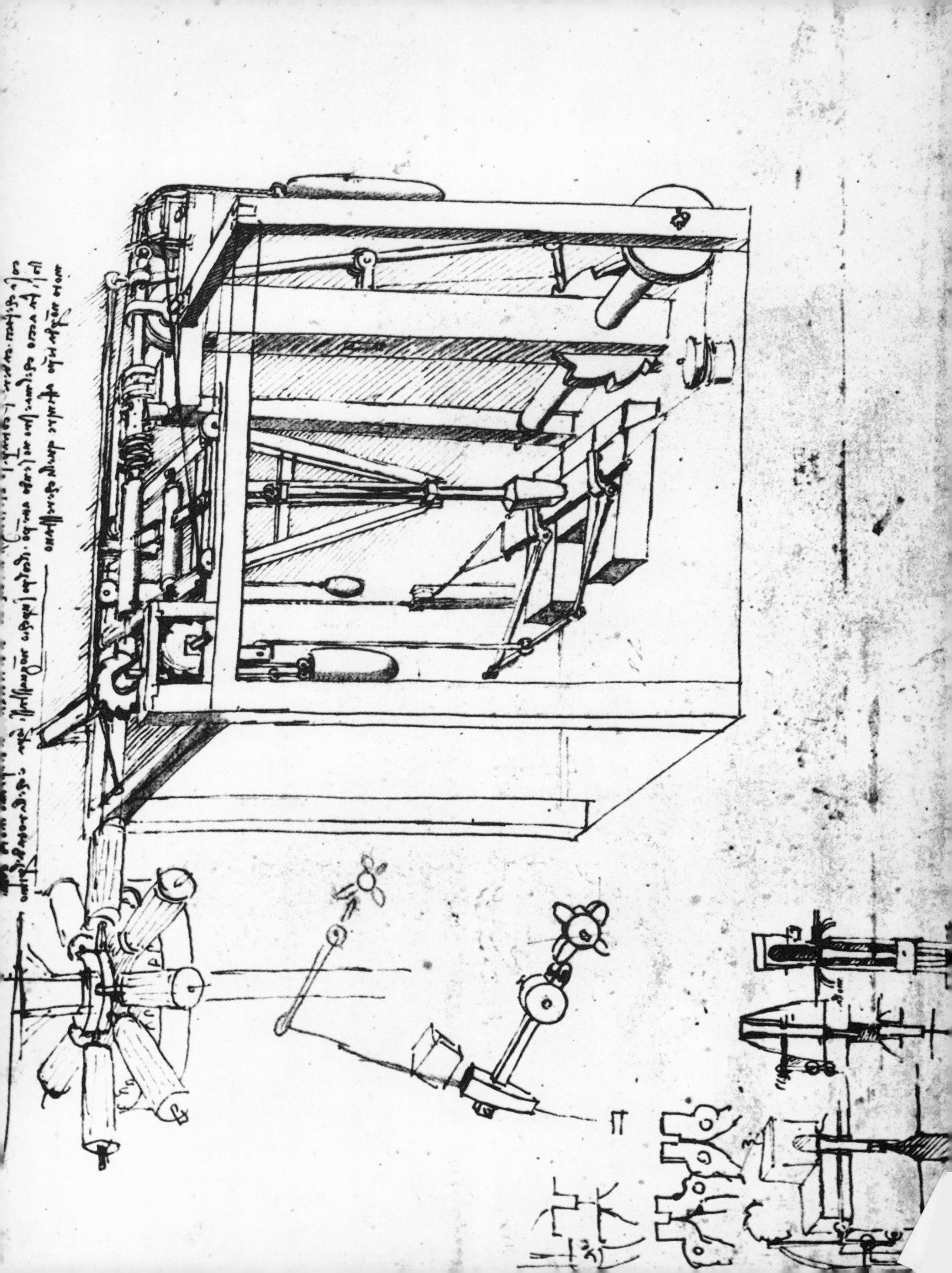

III

"Man Is the Image of the World"

1

A

[illegible]

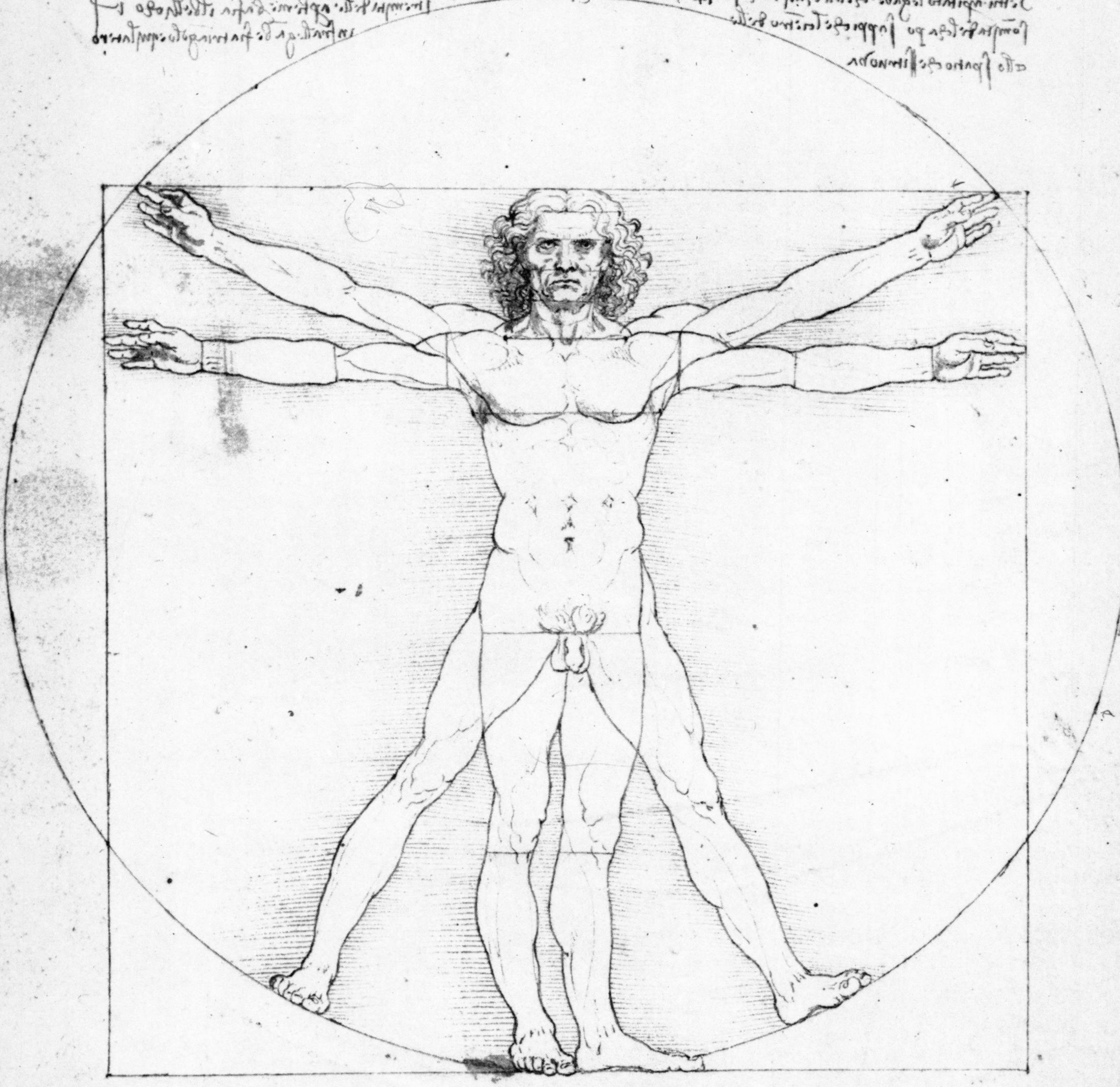

[illegible]

B

"Man has been called by the ancients," Leonardo wrote, "a lesser world," but instead of interpreting the idea astrologically, in terms of horoscopes and planetary influences on the lives of men, as was done by so many of his contemporaries, he used it imaginatively to express his feeling of man's relation to nature. He symbolically compared the human skeleton, the "stay and framework for the flesh," with the rocky core of the world as "the support of earth," and the blood of man and his breathing to the ocean with its tides, "the breathing of the world," and as the blood fills "the veins which spread their branches through the human body, so the ocean fills the body of the earth with an infinite number of veins of water."

There runs through his work an undercurrent of reverence for life so profound that it enabled him to carry out his systematic dissections and record what he saw with such clarity and loving detail that there is no horror in his anatomical drawings, only an overwhelming sense of the mysteries of life in all its diverse manifestations. "He who does not value life does not deserve it," he wrote, and no one ever valued it more intensely than he. He found the forces of life at work everywhere and was filled with wonder and a growing conviction that there was an underlying unity throughout the natural world of which man is a part. It was his search for the principles of this unity that made him so diverse, his mind ranging from speculations on the structure of the sun and the speed of light to mundane matters of plumbing and heating, and the further mechanization of such crafts as weaving and file making. It was for this reason that he gave equal care to the study of the tongue of a woodpecker and the hand of a man.

His creative imagination enabled him to recognize the inner relations of things which might outwardly appear dissimilar. He saw the same principles at work in the use of the muscles and sinews of man and animal as in the function of machines, and felt that everything was subject to the same forces which govern the flow of water and the revolutions of the earth. It was this that gave him the conviction that "every action has a cause," and that the constant and rhythmic interplay of action and reaction is expressed everywhere in nature. It gave him a view of time "as a continuous quantity," infinitely divisible and infinitely extendible, having reality for man in its relation to his experience, but having a scope far beyond the limitations of human lives. "The water you touch in a river," he wrote, "is the last of that which has passed, and the first of that which is coming. It is thus with time present."

Proportions of the Human Figure after Vitruvius, c. 1492. Pen and ink, 13⅛″×9⅝″. "The architect Vitruvius," Leonardo wrote on this drawing, "states in his work on architecture that the measurements of a man are arranged by Nature thus: four fingers make one palm, and four palms make one foot, six palms make one cubit, four cubits make once a man's height, four cubits make a pace, and twenty-four palms make a man's height, and these measurements are in his buildings." Academy, Venice

He saw all nature as a constant pulse and flow, "the end of one thing is the beginning of another." He saw this movement everywhere, and believed that it was "the cause of all life." Thus the reality of time was in its passing, just as the reality of the river was in its flowing, and the important thing was to study the patterns of that flow, because those patterns were the expression of the forces which govern the flow, the laws of nature that rule its diversity and give it coherence and order. A knowledge of them, he believed, allows us to understand something both of nature and of ourselves as "lesser worlds," and enables us to use what we know, as he did in his innumerable drawings of various observations and devices, for the benefit of man.

Throughout Leonardo's drawings and paintings there is a recurrence of dynamically curved lines, frequently forming a spiral, the one figure that fascinated him more than any other because of its expression of motion. He found it in the patterns of growth of trees and plants, in the interweaving of currents of water, in the plaiting of hair, in the shape of shells. It appears in the interlacing of the branches of trees which he painted on the vaulted ceiling of a room in the castle in Milan and in the mazelike designs that recur in his notebooks. He used it in his architectural studies for monumental staircases, and applied it to his design for a helicopter. For him such complex curving forms were a symbol of the continuous flow of nature, the constant act of becoming that he discovered everywhere. His figures of men in action move with twisting violence, and the struggling group of horsemen in *The Battle of Anghiari* wheel in a desperately circling mass. He drew the leaves of flowers and grasses in the curling dynamic forms similar to those he found in the

Study for *Leda and the Swan,* c. 1506. Pen and ink over black chalk. This and many other drawings, including many of his finest flower and plant studies, were done for a painting last heard of at Fontainebleau toward the end of the seventeenth century. Windsor; reproduced by gracious permission of Her Majesty the Queen

Oak Leaves with Acorns and Dyer's Greenweed. Red chalk touched with white on pink prepared paper. Windsor; reproduced by gracious permission of Her Majesty the Queen

ER
VII

structure of the body, with its interlace of tissues, its veins, nerves, and sinews. In an extraordinary group of drawings at Windsor Castle in which he envisioned a great convulsion of nature that destroys the earth, the devastating clouds, prophetic of an atomic blast, and the tidal waves of engulfing water take the same form of twisting, spiraling curves to express the endless change that he believed the only eternal constant.

Another drawing shows the figure of a man, and beside it is written in his distinctive hand, "Body formed from the perspective by Leonardo da Vinci, disciple of experience." For him art and science were not separate, but two means to the same end, knowledge, "the natural desire of good men." Perspective was a scientific method of visual analysis to arrive at knowledge. But that knowledge was not confined to the external aspects of things, because, as he advised the young artist in his incomplete book on painting, "A figure is not worthy of praise unless it serves to express the passion of the soul." Art for him was concerned with the inner life as well as the outward appearance. It was the function of the artist to reveal the one through the other, that revelation which gives every work of Leonardo a unique quality all its own. Experience was the key. As the "disciple of experience" he learned by careful observation, without preconceived no-

Study for *The Battle of Anghiari,* 1503–4. Pen and ink. Academy, Venice

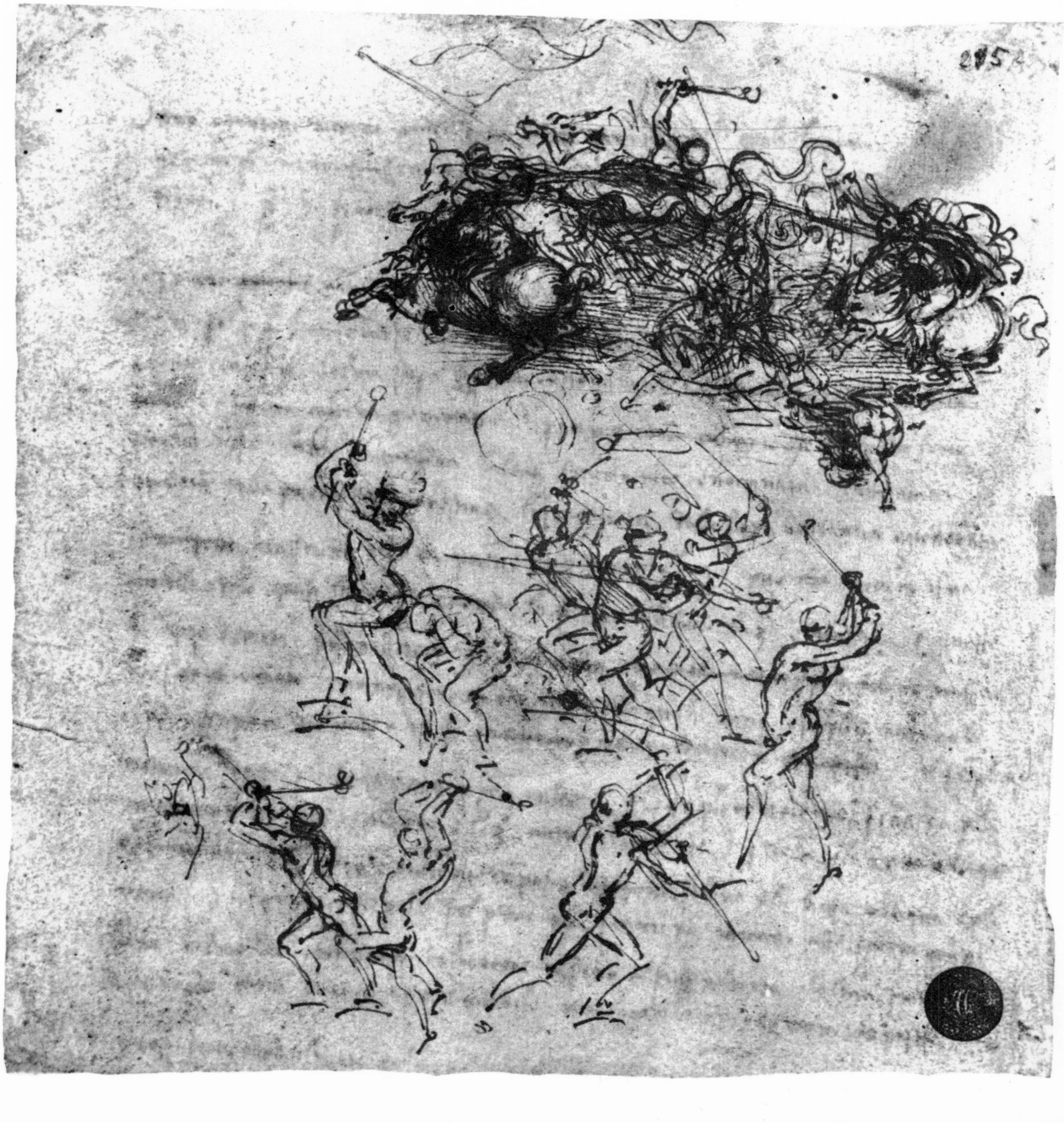

tions, in a process enlivened and given insight by the imagination, in a search for that essential reality. Thus through his art he had the purpose and the approach of the modern scientist, the quest for truth pursued with vigilant objectivity.

He had faith that the mind of man could know the truth and he did not fear it, no matter how vast or impersonal, for "Truth," he wrote, "was the only daughter of Time." It was thus inevitable that he was a lonely man, and his lifelong search a solitary one. His was an imagination that could not only embrace the medieval vision of the destruction of the world, as illustrated in his drawings at Windsor, and the modern concepts of relative time and infinite space, but also envision things to come. "Science," he wrote, "is the knowledge of things possible," and on that he based what he called "prescience, the knowledge of things which may come to pass, though but slowly." Many of his ideas have been realized, some have proven impractical, while others still await their time. The intervening years have all too often shown the cruelty of man that he deplored and considered such an unworthy betrayal of the richness of potentiality with which nature has endowed him. But in the centuries-old struggle of man toward freedom of the mind, his lifelong quest marked a turning point in history, for he was the pioneer and the great precursor of the modern world.

Cloudburst, after 1514. Black chalk. Windsor; reproduced by gracious permission of Her Majesty the Queen

When on the second of May, 1519, Leonardo died at the Manor of Cloux, his fellow Tuscan, Vasari, the artistic biographer of his age, wrote that "the loss of Leonardo was mourned out of all measure by all who had known him . . . and as Florence had the greatest of gifts in his birth, so she suffered an infinite loss in his death." Even today men are still finding new evidence of the genius that enabled him to transcend his own era and become a man of all times, whose life and achievements are a constant reminder of the infinite possibilities of the human spirit. As George Sarton has written, "Leonardo saw clearly five hundred years ago what very few people are able to see today, and the few who do see it can do so only because they stand on his shoulders."

An Embryo in the Uterus, c. 1512. Pen and ink. This is one of the first renderings of the subject in history, and was done as a part of the extraordinary anatomical research to gather material for a projected book "to commence with the conception of man" and then go on through all the stages of human development. "Would that it might please our Creator," Leonardo wrote, "that I were able to reveal the nature of man and his customs even as I describe his figure." Windsor; reproduced by gracious permission of Her Majesty the Queen

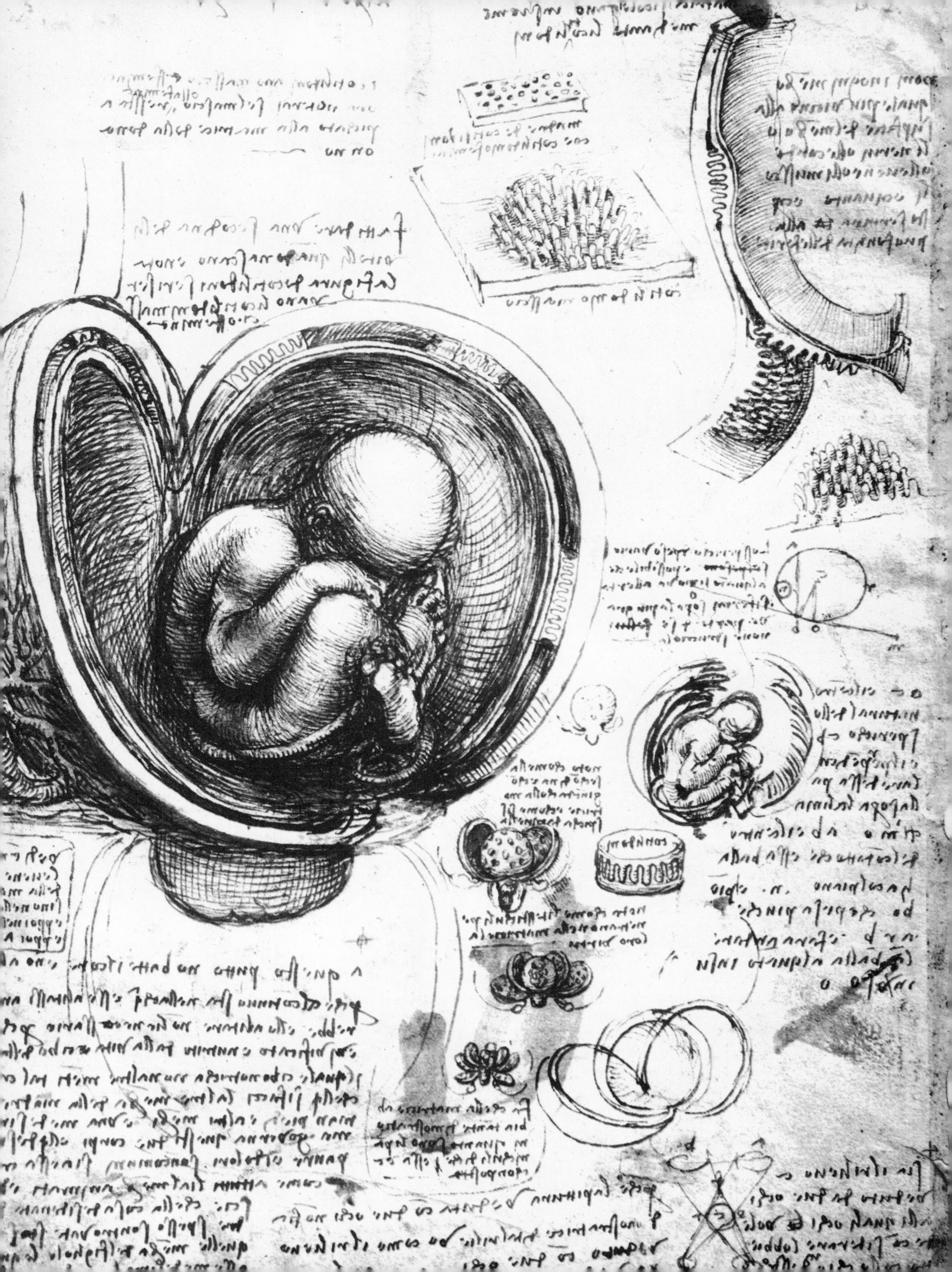

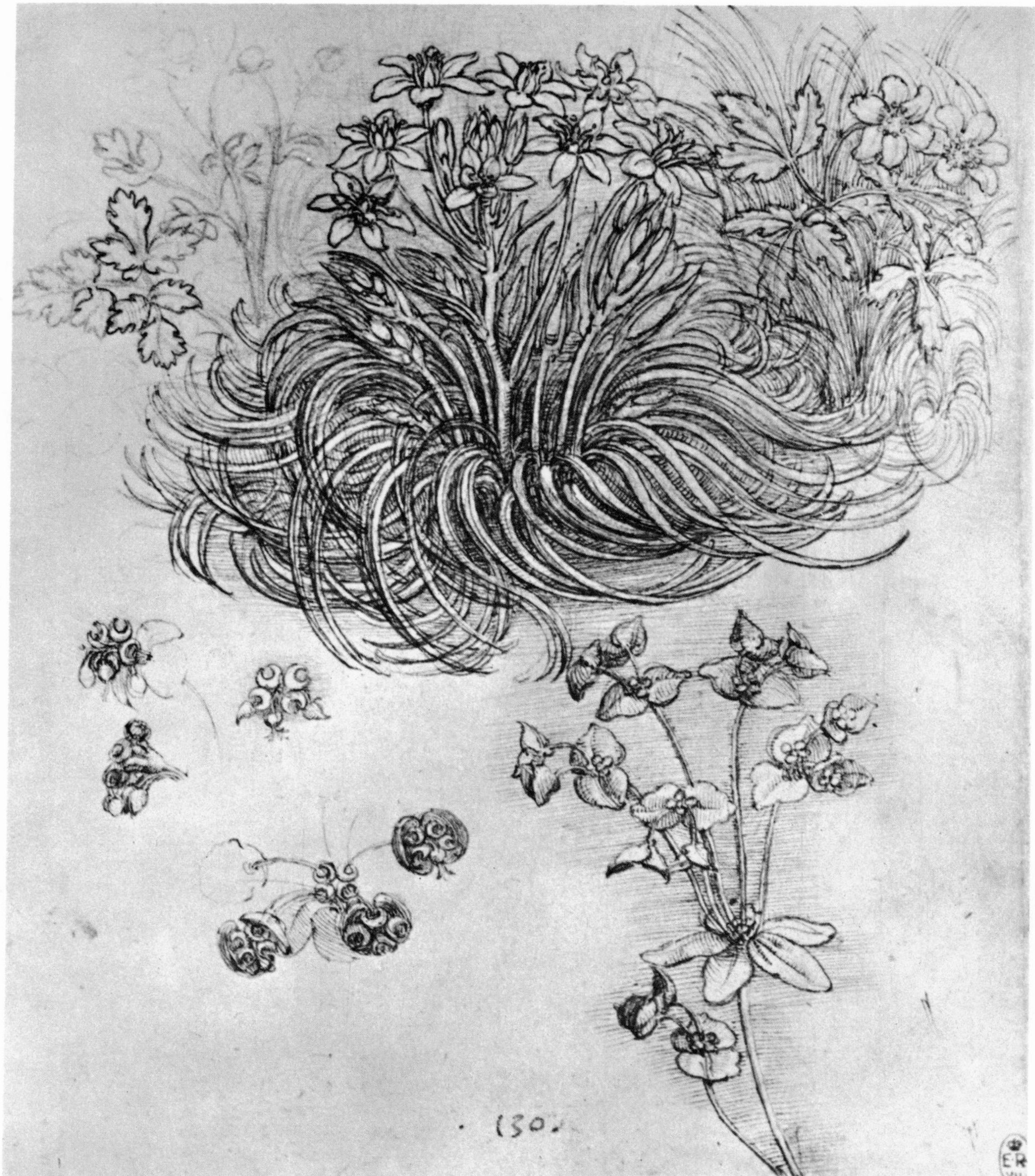

A Star of Bethlehem and Other Plants, c. 1505–8. Red chalk and pen and ink. Throughout his life Leonardo made studies of plants. Among them all, Sir Kenneth Clark, in his biography, selects this as "a masterpiece . . . which combines the rhythmic movement of his hand with the microscopic steadiness of his eye, so that it becomes an essential token of his art when freed from all conscious intentions, dramatic or professional." Windsor; reproduced by gracious permission of Her Majesty the Queen

Studies of Water, c. 1510. Pen and ink. "Water which falls from a height into other water," Leonardo noted, "imprisons within itself a certain quantity of air, and this through the force of the blow becomes submerged with it. Then with swift movement it rises up again and arrives at the surface . . . clothed with a fine veil of moisture spherical in form, and proceeds by circles away from the spot where it first struck." Windsor; reproduced by gracious permission of Her Majesty the Queen

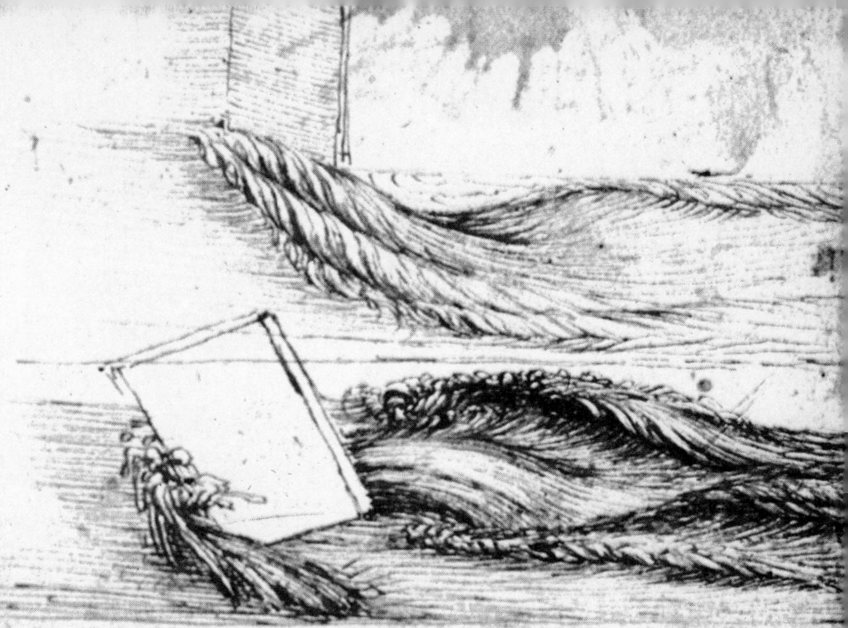

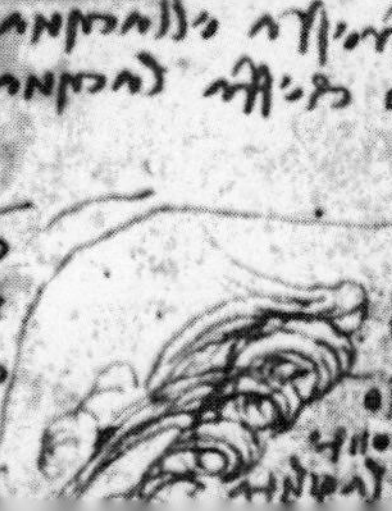

Pages 178–79: Studies in Expression: Horses, a Lion, a Man, c. 1503–4. Pen and ink. One of many drawings in preparation for the lost fresco of *The Battle of Anghiari.* Windsor; reproduced by gracious permission of Her Majesty the Queen

Leonardo's Self-portrait, c. 1512. Red chalk, 13⅛″ × 8⅜″. Royal Library, Turin

Deluge, c. 1517. Black chalk and brown and yellow inks. Leonardo was haunted in later years with visions of cosmic destruction, forming the subject of a number of drawings done after he went to France in 1516, of which this is the climax. Here all the forces of nature loosed in fury are reduced to the abstract forms expressive of their limitless power. Windsor; reproduced by gracious permission of Her Majesty the Queen

IMPORTANT DATES IN LEONARDO'S LIFE AND TIMES

HIS LIFE

1452: in April Leonardo is born at Anchiano, near Vinci, in Tuscany, the illegitimate son of Ser Piero da Vinci, a young lawyer, and Caterina, a village girl.

1469: Leonardo is living in Florence, apprenticed to Andrea Verrocchio.

1472: completes Verrocchio's painting of *The Baptism of Christ,* now in the Uffizi Museum in Florence, and is admitted to the Guild of St. Luke as a painter.

1473: draws a landscape of the Arno Valley on August 5, his first dated work.

1476: still in Verrocchio's studio as an assistant and collaborator.

1478: first independent commission, an uncompleted altarpiece for the government of Florence. Begins the *Benois Madonna* and the *Madonna Litta,* now in the Hermitage, Leningrad.

1480: gains the patronage of Lorenzo de' Medici, the ruler of Florence.

1481: commissioned to paint an *Adoration of the Magi* for the monastery of S. Donato a Scopeto near Florence. Never completed, it is now in the Uffizi.

1481–82: goes to Milan as painter and engineer to Duke Ludovico Sforza, and to sculpture an equestrian monument of Francesco Sforza, the duke's father.

1483: contracts to paint *The Virgin of the Rocks* now in the Louvre; a later version is in the National Gallery in London. Paints the portrait of Cecilia Gallerani, identified as *The Lady with the Ermine* in Cracow.

HIS TIMES

1453: the fall of Constantinople to the Turks ends the Eastern Empire after a thousand years.

1464: Cosimo de' Medici dies and is succeeded by his son Piero.

1469: Giuliano and Lorenzo de' Medici inherit the leadership of Florence on the death of their father, Piero.

1471: Pope Sixtus IV

1473: Nicolaus Copernicus, the famous astronomer, born in Poland.

1475: Michelangelo Buonarroti born at Caprese in Tuscany.

1478: the Pazzi conspiracy to overthrow the Medici: Giuliano is murdered at high mass in the cathedral, but Lorenzo the Magnificent survives, though wounded; war with Naples and the pope follows.

1479: Ludovico il Moro usurps the duchy of Milan from his nephew, Gian Galeazzo Sforza.

1483: Raphael Sanzio born at Urbino.

1484: Pope Innocent VIII

HIS LIFE

1487: designs the pageant of *Il Paradiso* with its revolving stage, and works on designs for the central tower of the cathedral of Milan until the following year.

1489: working on anatomical research.

1490: recommences work on the equestrian monument. Goes to Pavia with Francesco di Giorgio, stays to study mathematics and architecture.

1493: the full-scale model of the equestrian monument is exhibited at the time of the wedding of Bianca Maria Sforza and the Emperor Maximilian.

1495: starts work in the refectory of S. Maria delle Grazie in Milan on *The Last Supper,* which is nearly finished by the end of 1497.

1498: paints the Sala delle Asse in the Sforza Castle.

1499: in April Duke Ludovico gives Leonardo a vineyard near Milan. In December Leonardo flees Milan at the duke's downfall.

1500: visits Mantua, where he draws the portrait of the Duchess Isabella d'Este, goes to Venice in February, and returns to Florence in the spring.

1501: at work on *The Madonna and Child with St. Anne,* the drawing for which is now in the National Gallery in London, while the painting is in the Louvre. He is also at work on the lost *Madonna with the Yarn Winder,* and has several pupils.

1502: military engineer for Cesare Borgia, son of Pope Alexander VI, and captain-general of the papal armies.

1503: begins the cartoon for the fresco of *The Battle of Anghiari* commissioned by the government of Florence for the grand council chamber of the Palazzo della Signoria, works on the *Mona Lisa,* now in the Louvre, and carries on dissections and anatomical studies.

1504: one of those appointed to decide the best place for Michelangelo's statue of *David.*

1505: cartoon for *The Battle of Anghiari* finished.

HIS TIMES

1488: Verrocchio dies in Florence.

1492: Columbus' first voyage to the New World. Lorenzo the Magnificent dies and is succeeded by his ineffectual son, Pietro. Rodrigo Borgia elected pope as Alexander VI.

1494: Charles VIII of France invades Italy, briefly occupies Florence, and, the following year, Naples. The Dominican monk, Savonorola, institutes a reform government in Florence after the banishment of the Medici.

1498: Savonorola hanged and burnt in the Piazza della Signoria in Florence.

1499: the French under Louis XII invade Italy and capture Milan. Michelangelo completes his *Pietà* in the Vatican.

1500: Duke Ludovico counterattacks, loses, is captured by the French and imprisoned in the Château of Loches, where he dies in 1508.

1501–2: Second voyage of Amerigo Vespucci to the New World, the published account of which led to its being named America after him.

1503: Pope Julius II, patron of Raphael and Michelangelo.

1504: Michelangelo starts work on the cartoon for a fresco for the Palazzo della Signoria in Florence, commissioned as a pendant to Leonardo's *Battle of Anghiari;* neither reached completion.

HIS LIFE		HIS TIMES	
1506:	obtains permission of the Florentine government to leave *The Battle of Anghiari* fresco, never to be finished, and return to Milan to work on projects for Charles d'Amboise, the French governor of the city, and designs another equestrian monument, for Gian Giacomo Trivulzio, his successor.	1506:	Construction begins on St. Peter's in Rome.
1507:	appointed painter and engineer to King Louis XII of France, and in September returns to Florence.		
1508:	back in Milan for further anatomical studies and other research.	1508:	Michelangelo starts work on his Sistine Chapel frescoes.
1510–11:	anatomical research with the young Marc Antonio dalla Torre who came to be considered the greatest anatomist of his time.		
		1512:	Michelangelo completes the Sistine ceiling. Raphael finishes his frescoes of *The School of Athens* and *The Disputation of the Sacrament* in the Vatican.
1513:	leaves Milan for Florence and then for Rome where he is given apartments in the Belvedere of the Vatican under the patronage of Giuliano de' Medici, Duke of Nemours, son of Lorenzo the Magnificent, and brother of Pope Leo X.	1513:	Giovanni de' Medici, son of Lorenzo the Magnificent, elected pope as Leo X.
1515:	visits Parma.	1515:	Francis I succeeds to the throne of France.
1516–17:	to France as "First Painter and Engineer to the King of France"; lives in the Manor of Cloux, the gift of Francis I, who holds court at the Château of Amboise nearby.	1516:	Giuliano de' Medici, Duke of Nemours, son of Lorenzo and patron of Leonardo, dies.
1517:	visited by the Cardinal of Aragon, who saw his paintings and many manuscripts.	1517:	Raphael starts work on *The Transfiguration,* left unfinished at his death at thirty-seven in 1520. Michelangelo in Florence working on the unfinished façade of S. Lorenzo and planning the Medici Chapel.
1518:	reception at Cloux for the wedding of the king's niece to Lorenzo de' Medici, Duke of Urbino and brother of Leo X.		
1519:	Leonardo dies at Cloux on May 2d and is buried in the Church of St.-Florentin in Amboise.		

A SHORT LIST OF BOOKS

On Leonardo:

* Sir Kenneth Clark: *Leonardo da Vinci, An Account of His Development as an Artist,* Penguin, Baltimore, 1960.

———: *A Catalogue of the Drawings of Leonardo da Vinci in the Collection of His Majesty the King at Windsor Castle,* 2 vols., Cambridge University Press, 1935.

Bern Dibner: *Leonardo da Vinci, Military Engineer,* Burndy Library, New York, 1946.

Ludwig Goldscheider, *Leonardo da Vinci,* Phaidon, New York and London, 1959.

Ivor B. Hart: *The World of Leonardo da Vinci, Man of Science, Engineer, and Dreamer of Flight,* Viking, New York, 1961.

Edward MacCurdy: *The Mind of Leonardo da Vinci,* Tudor, New York, 1948.

* A. E. Popham: *The Drawings of Leonardo da Vinci,* Harcourt, Brace & World, New York, 1945.

Leonardo da Vinci, Reynal & Co., New York, 1956. A collection of essays with many illustrations on various aspects of his career by a group of authors; published as a result of the memorial exhibition in Milan in 1952.

Leonardo's Own Writings:

Edward MacCurdy: *The Notebooks of Leonardo da Vinci,* various editions.

Jean Paul and Irma A. Richter: *The Literary Works of Leonardo da Vinci,* revised and enlarged edition, 2 vols., Oxford University Press, New York and London.

Carlo Pedretti (ed.): *Leonardo da Vinci on Painting: A Lost Book,* University of California Press, Berkeley, 1964.

Irma A. Richter: *Selections from the Notebooks of Leonardo da Vinci,* Oxford University Press, New York and London, 1952.

* Pamela Taylor: *The Notebooks of Leonardo da Vinci, A New Selection,* Mentor, New York, 1960.

From 1923 through 1936 the Commissione Vinciana published reproductions of all known Leonardo manuscripts with transcriptions of the original Italian. The several very large volumes are available in many libraries.

General Background:

* Jacob C. Burckhardt: *The Civilization of the Renaissance in Italy,* revised edition, Phaidon, London and New York, 1950.

* Bernard Berenson: *Italian Painters of the Renaissance,* Phaidon, New York and London, 1953.

———: *Italian Pictures of the Renaissance,* 2 vols., Phaidon, London and New York, 1957.

———: *The Drawings of the Florentine Painters,* 3 vols., University of Chicago Press, 1938.

Horizon Book of the Renaissance, Doubleday, Garden City, 1961.

* Walter Pater, *The Renaissance,* various editions.

* *The Renaissance, Six Essays,* Harper Torchbooks, New York, 1962. See especially those by Sarton and Panofsky.

* Ferdinand Schevill, *The Medici,* Harper Torchbooks, New York, 1960.

Sections on the Renaissance in:

John Canaday: *Metropolitan Seminars in Art,* "The High Renaissance," 2d Series, Portfolio F.

Ernst Gombrich: *The Story of Art,* tenth edition, Phaidon, New York.

H. W. Janson: *History of Art,* Abrams, New York.

John A. Symonds: the sections on "The Revival of Learning" and "The Fine Arts" from *The Renaissance in Italy,* Modern Library and other editions.

* Giorgio Vasari: *The Lives of the Painters, Sculptors, and Architects,* translated by A. B. Hind, 4 vols., Dutton, New York, 1927.

*** Either in paperback or available in paperback.**

Scientific Background:

George Sarton: *Six Wings, Men of Science in the Renaissance,* Indiana University Press, Bloomington, 1957.

* Charles Singer: *From Magic to Science,* Dover, New York, 1957.

———, and others: *A History of Technology,* 5 vols., Oxford University Press, New York and London, 1954–58.

* ———: *A Short History of Scientific Ideas,* Oxford University Press, New York and London, 1959.

* Abbott Payson Usher: *A History of Mechanical Inventions,* Harvard University Press, Cambridge, 1954.

* Either in paperback or available in paperback.

INDEX

Abbaco, Benedetto d', 29
Adoration of the Magi, 27, *77,* 183
Adoration of the Shepherds, *26*
Agiropoulos, John, 29
Airplanes. *See* Flight; Flying machines
Alberti, Leon Battista, 27, 74
Alchemy, 146
Alexander VI, Pope, 51, 55, 184
Amboise, Charles d', 55, 185
Amboise, France, *67*
  Leonardo in, 57, 59, 174, 185
  restoration of Manor in, 14
Anatomy, *73–75, 81–85*
  of birds and bats, 135, 142
  first dissections, 74
  ideal human proportions, 74, *168*
  Leonardo's dissections, 39, 57, 74–75, 169, 184, 185
  of woman, *85, 175*
Animals, *22, 24, 26, 58*
  Leonardo's fascination with, 23
  See also Horses
  See also Churches; Fortifications
Archimedes' screw, 87, *94–95,* 146
Architecture, 39, *40,* 41, *47*
Aristotelian theory, 19
Arkwright, Sir Richard, 149, 160
Armored vehicle, 28, 105, *109*
Arno River, canalization of, 89
Arno Valley (drawing), *30–31,* 183
Art, Leonardo's conception of, 72, 172
Artillery. *See Ballistae;* Bombards; Cannon
Astronomy, 18, 71, 150
  Leonardo's concepts of, 18
Automation, Leonardo's anticipation of, 145, 151

Ballistae, 104, 105, *111, 117*
Balloons, 136, 137
Baptism of Christ (Verrocchio), 26, 183
Baroncelli, Bernardo di Bandino, 27, 28
Battle of Anghiari, The, 54, 55, 170, *172, 178–79,* 184, 185
Benois Madonna, 183
Bird's-eye views, *73,* 79, 137
Bombards, 106, *114, 121*
Borgia, Cesare
  Leonardo in service of, 51, 54–55, 89, 184
  Leonardo's sketch of, 54–55, *60–61*
Braccio, defined, 79
Brahe, Tycho, 150
Bramante, 41
Bridges, 28, 91, 107, *129*
Brunelleschi, Filippo, 24, 72, 74

Caesar's *Gallic Wars,* 104
Canals, 12, 39, 59, *72*
  Leonardo's plans for, 89, 91, *97, 99*
  machines for digging of, *101, 163*
Cannon, 28, 105–7, *121*
  construction of *102,* 106, *120,* 151
    metal-drawing machine for, 149, *157*
  earliest, 104
  lifting devices for, 146, *152*
  multiple-firing, *106, 123*
  steam, 106, *126*
Cardano, Girolamo, 11, 75
Catapults, 28, 103, 104, 105, *117, 119*
Cats, *22, 24*
Cayley, Sir George, 137
Cellini, Benvenuto, 59, 164
Chariots
  with flails, 105, *111*
  scythed, 105, *109–10*
Churches, 41, *45, 78*
City planning, *40,* 41
Clark, Sir Kenneth, 13, 176
Clocks, 149–*50*
  alarm, 151
Clockwork mechanism, *144,* 151, *155*
Cloudburst (drawing), *173*
Cogged wheels, *148, 153*
Colors, techniques for making, 25
Columbus, Christopher, 27, 184

NOTE: Page references to drawings are in italics.

Convection, principle of, *155*
Cosmic destruction, 172, 173, *181*
Cranes, 91, *101*, *163*
Crossbows
development of, 103–4
Leonardo's plans for, 105
giant crossbow, 105, *113*
multiple crossbows, *116*

Dante, Alighieri, 23
Darius (Verrocchio), Leonardo's drawing from, *33*
David (Verrocchio), 26
Deluge. *See* Cosmic destruction
Diving, 51, *90*, 91, 148
Dogs, *24*, *58*
anatomy of, *82*
Donatello, 24
Dragons, *22*, *56–57*, *63*
Drapery, *64*
Dredges, *89*, 91
Dürer, Albrecht, 72, 75

Earth-moving machine, *163*
Embryo, *175*
Equestrian monuments
Sforza, 28, *36*, 38–39, *44*, *46*, 183, 184
Trivulzio, 55, *65*, 185
Este, Isabella d', 184

Fiesole, 24, 137
File-making machine, *144*, 147, 151
Flight, principles of, 135, 146
Florence
canalization project for, 89
cathedral of, 25
compared with Milan, 12
described, 23–24
Leonardo in, 24–28, 51, 183, 184–85
Flowers. *See* Plants and flowers
Flying machines, *134–43*, 146, 151
Fortifications, 104–5, *107*, *132–33*
development of artillery and, 107, 133
See also Siege devices
Fossils, 55, 87
Foundry, cannon, *102*. *See also* Cannon, construction of
Francis I, King of France, 67, 185
Leonardo's service under, 57, 59, 91, 195
French invasion of Italy, 39, 41, 184
Friction, 146, 148

Galen, 74
Galileo, 18
Gallerani, Cecilia, 183
Gas attack, 107
Gear systems, 148–49, *153*, *161*
Geology, 87, *93*
Giacomo da Ferrara, 51
Gille, Bertrand, 145
Giorgio, Francesco di, 105, 184
Giotto, 23
Gravity, 146
Greek Fire, 104, 105
Gribeauval, General Vaquette de, 151
Gunpowder, 104

Hammer, automatic, 151, *165*
Hands, *32*
Hegetor of Byzantium, 104
Helicopter, *135–36*
Hodometer, *150*
Horses, *63*, *125*
chariots drawn by, *109–11*
for Sforza monument, *36*, 38, *44*
for *The Battle of Anghiari*, *54*, 55, *178–79*
for Trivulzio monument, *65*

Jefferson, Thomas, 151
Julius II, Pope, 55, 184

Kopernik, Nicolaus (Copernicus), 18, 183

Ladders, scaling, 107, *127*
repelling of, *128*
Lady with the Ermine, The, 183
Lances, *125*
Landscapes, *30–31*, *67*, *72*, *73*, *79*, *86*
Last Supper, The, 39, *39*, *47–49*, 184
Lateran Council, Second, 104
Lathes, 149, *161*
Leda and the Swan, *170*
Lenormand, Louis Sébastien, 137
Lenses, 71, 148
Leo X, Pope, 55–57, 91, 185
Leonardo da Vinci
apprenticeship of, 24–26, *30–31*, 183
boyhood of, 23–24
in Cesare Borgia's service, 51, 54–55, 89, 184
character of, 17
chronology of, 183–85
death of, 174, 185
education of, 25–26, 29
as experimental scientist, 29, 145–46, 172–73
in French service, 55, 57, 59, 185
Lorenzo and, 27–28, 183
in Ludovico's service, 28–29, 38–41, 89, 183, 184
as musician, 28–29
notebooks of, 17, 19
influence of, 75
mediums used in, 13
modern collections of, 13, 14
purpose of, 11–12
possible travels of, 26–27
in Rome, 55–57, 185
self-portrait of, *180*
Life, Leonardo's reverence for, 169

NOTE: Page references to drawings are in italics.

Life preserver, *91*
Lifting devices, 146, 149, *152*
Loire canal system, 91
Long bow, 104
Louis XII, King of France, 41, 55, 184

Machines, *144–65*. *See also* Flying machines; Military engineering; specific types of machines
Madonna and Child with St. Anne, The, 64, 137, 184
Madonna Litta, 34, 183
Madonna with the Yarn Winder, 184
Mangonels, 28, 103, 105, *118*
Mantua, Leonardo in, 184
Masquerader in Costume (drawing), *66*
Mathematics, Leonardo on, 146
Maudsley, Henry, 147
Maximilian (Holy Roman Emperor), 38, 184
Measurement, machines for, 150
Mechanical lion, 59
Medici, Cosimo de', 24, 183
Medici, Giuliano de' (brother of Lorenzo), 28, 183
Medici, Giuliano de' (son of Lorenzo; Duke of Nemours), 55–57, 185
Medici, Lorenzo de' (Duke of Urbino), 59
Medici, Lorenzo de' (the Magnificent), 27–28, 183
Melzi, Orazio, 11
Michelangelo Buonarroti, 23, 74, 183, 184
  Battle of Cascina, 55
  Sistine frescoes, 56, 185
Milan
  cathedral of, 41, 184
  compared with Florence, 12
  described, 37
  Leonardo in, 12, 37–39, 41, 51, 55, 89, 149, 170, 183–84, 185
Military engineering, 103–*33*. *See also* specific weapons and devices
  development of, 103–5
  Leonardo's purpose in, 103
  Leonardo's work in, 28, 51, 105–7
  profession of, 105
Milling machine, 151
Mint machinery, 151, *165*
Mirrors, 71, 148, 156
Mona Lisa, 55, 137, 184
Monge, Gaspard, 74
Montgolfier brothers, 137
Mortars (bombards), 106, *114, 121*

Naples, 28
Nature, Leonardo's view of, 169–70
Naval warfare
  Greek Fire in, 104
  underwater attack on ships, 51, *90,* 91, 148
Neptune in His Chariot (drawing), *52–53*
Newton, Sir Isaac, 18, 71, 146

Old Man Meditating (drawing), *88*
Olive-oil press, 149, *161*
Orthogonal projection, 74

Pacioli, Luca, 39, 51
  The Divine Proportion, 72
    Leonardo's illustration for, *70*
Painting as a window, 72
Panofsky, Irwin, 75
Parachutes, 135–37
Parma, Lorenzo in, 185
Paul, Jean, 13
Paul, Lewis, 149, 160
Pendulum, 149–50
Perpetual motion, 146
Perspective, *70*–74, 76, 79, 172
  aerial, *73,* 79, 137
Pitons, 107, *127*
Plants and flowers, *43, 61, 171, 176*
Ponte Vecchio (Florence), 24
Pontine Marshes, 91
Popham, A. E., 13
Printing presses, 149, *154*

Raphael Sanzio, 56, 183–85
Renaissance, 17–19
  artistic view in, 72
Richter, Irma A., 13
Romagna, 89
Rome, Leonardo in, 55–57, 185
Romorantin, France, 59

St. George and the Dragon, 63
St. Peter's Cathedral (Rome), 41, 55, 56, 185
Sarton, George, 103, 174
Scaling ladders, 107, *127*
  repelling of, *128*
Screw
  Archimedes', 87, *94–95,* 146
  principle of, 146–48
Screw-cutting machine, 146–*47*
Scythed chariots, 105, *109–10*
Segni, Antonio, 54
Sforza, Francesco, equestrian monument to, 28, *36,* 38–39, *44, 46,* 183, 184
Sforza, Ludovico, 37–38, 183
  defeat and death of, 41, 184
  Leonardo's letter to, 28–29
  Leonardo's service with, 38–41, 89, 183, 184
Sheet-metal machine, 149, *156*
Shields, *115*
Siege devices, 28, 104
  scaling ladders, 107, *127*
    repelling of, *128*
  tortoises, 104
  towers, 107, *131*
Silk machinery, 149
Skull, *81*
  wax-injection method in study of, 74–75
Spiral, Leonardo's use of, *88,* 170, 172, *173, 177, 181*
Springs, 151
  in military weapons, *105, 119*

NOTE: Page references to drawings are in italics.

Stables, *40,* 41
Stage sets, 38, 73, 184
Storm Breaking over an Alpine Valley (drawing), *86*
Swimming under water, 91

Telescopes, 71
Terry, Eli, 151
Textile machines, 149, 151, *158, 159*
Torre, Marc Antonio dalla, 75, 185
Tortoises (siege machines), 104
Toscanelli, Paolo, 27
Trabocchi (*trébushets*), 28, 103
Translations of Leonardo's works, 13, 187
Tree, *80*. *See also* Landscapes
Trivulzio, Gian Giacomo, monument of, 55, *65,* 185
Turnspits, 149, *155*

Usher, Abbott Payson, 145
  Introduction by, 11–12

Valturio, Roberto, *On Things Military,* 105, 107
Vasari, Giorgio, 51, 174
Vauban, Marshal de, 107
Venice, Leonardo in, 51, 91, 184
Verrocchio, Andrea del
  Baptism of Christ, 26, 183
  Darius, Leonardo's drawing from, *33*
  David, 26
  death of, 184
  Leonardo's apprenticeship with, 24–26, *30–31,* 183

Vesalius, Andreas, *The Structure of the Human Body,* 75
Vespucci, Amerigo, 27, 184
Vinci, described, 23
Virgin and Holy Children, The, 42
Virgin of the Rocks, The, 35, 42, 183
Vitelli, General, 55
Vitruvius, 104, 148, 150
  ideal human proportions of, *168*

War
  Leonardo's opinion of, 103
  See also Military engineering
Water
  device for walking on, *91*
  devices for raising, 87, *94–95*
  Leonardo's studies of, 87–*88,* 89, *177*
  See also Canals
Water pipes, boring of, 147–48
Water wheels, 87
  perpetual-motion, 146
Wax-injection method in anatomy, 74–75
Well-drilling machines, *148*
Whitney, Eli, 151
Woman's anatomy, *85, 175*
Woodcarving techniques, 24–25
Woolens, machinery for production of, 149, 151, *158, 159*
Wright brothers, 137

NOTE: Page references to drawings are in italics.